TABLE OF CONTENTS

About the Authors...
NCTM Standards..
About This Book..
How to Use This Book..

D1454094

NCTM STANDARDS

Skills	Number and Operations	Algebra	Geometry	Measurement	Data Analysis and Probability
Addition	69, 82, 97, 134, 141, 185, 192, 196, 207, 236, 263, 265, 282	139, 140, 181	147, 201	98, 155	
Application	13, 34, 35, 62, 92, 149, 187, 233, 243	18, 137, 217, 223, 234, 239, 264, 266, 267, 250	5, 17, 20, 22, 27, 30, 38, 44, 59, 120, 128, 167, 191, 202, 208	9, 47, 159, 178, 195, 199, 238	138, 229, 232, 266, 276
Count	2, 8, 28, 37, 61, 70, 87, 88, 135, 168, 188, 211, 218, 240, 254, 255, 259, 273, 277	10	176, 194	7, 56, 86, 93, 136	
Fractions	122		268, 270	169, 271	
Language	16, 33, 43, 84, 85, 89, 90, 109, 111, 224, 244, 245, 246, 247, 249	79, 124, 227	4, 15, 21, 29, 39, 102, 106, 151, 170, 175, 213	58, 80, 91, 119, 123, 158, 179	161, 231, 237, 269, 272, 280, 281,
Logic	46, 65, 115, 126, 129, 187, 203, 206, 210, 215	71, 83, 152	32, 64, 94, 127, 204, 222, 249	68, 116, 121, 130, 165, 225, 273	117, 162, 180, 182, 183, 219
Manipulative	57, 63, 76, 101, 226, 271	96, 283	186, 193, 256	78, 105, 279	
Match	6, 24, 26, 31, 36, 50, 60, 66, 100, 107, 110, 118, 144, 157, 184, 189, 205, 221, 228, 235, 241, 260, 261, 274, 275, 278	3	19, 23, 49, 55, 106, 230	104, 114, 145, 154, 209, 242	
Order	12, 25, 40, 41, 150, 172	99	11, 77	42, 45, 81, 156, 208, 262	243, 133
Pattern	74, 75, 108, 112, 113, 253, 258	1, 14, 52, 148, 163, 166, 177, 248, 252, 279	197	198, 200, 276	
Shape	125, 132, 160	171	53, 54, 131, 153, 251	216	
Subtraction	48, 51, 67, 72, 73, 142, 146, 164, 173, 190, 214, 220, 256		95, 174	103, 143, 212	257

About This Book

Teaching and practicing preschool math concepts and skills has never been easier! This unique all-in-one book allows parents to learn right along with their child—no lesson preparation needed! This will save you hours of time. Each section introduces a specific topic, followed by appropriate practice and application activities. The activities in this book are written to the standards of the National Council of Teachers of Mathematics (NCTM). Children enjoy the colorful, engaging challenges of the varying activities!

How to Use This Book

This book focuses on numbers 0-10. The skills and concepts presented in this book spiral throughout the book. That means that you will see a topic dealt with for a few pages and then a gap before it is covered again. We do that so your child has some time to develop and mature before dealing with more complex aspects of the skill/concept.

Our suggestion is that you proceed through this book page by page. A child who successfully finishes this book will know and apply the mathematics skills and concepts taught to most kindergartners.

Please note: Most 4-year-olds can be taught to add, subtract, and reason mathematically, but just as all children do not grow at the same rate, not all brains develop at the same rate. If your child struggles, don't be alarmed and jump to conclusions about the child's intelligence. Children's brains develop at different rates — especially young children. If your child has trouble identifying shapes, colors, or the concept of sets (groups), we suggest working with your child in *Building Thinking Skills® Beginning* before or concurrently with this book.

Teaching Suggestions

Keep learning fun and avoid frustrating your child. Work around your child's attention span. As a parent, you have a great advantage to teach young children because most young children love to spend time with Mom and Dad. If you keep learning fun, you will have an energetic pupil who looks forward to each and every lesson.

If your child struggles with the math taught in this book, we suggest both *Mathematical Reasoning® Beginning 1* (focuses on the numbers 0-5) and *Building Thinking Skills® Beginning* (focuses on shapes, colors, tracking, sets, visual discrimination, and geometric shapes). *Building Thinking Skills® Beginning* can also be used concurrently with this book to improve general thinking skills.

Using Concrete Objects: If your child struggles with an activity, you can come back to it later or try recreating the activity using objects your child can touch and feel (e.g. little blocks or counting bears). There is no one correct way to teach the skills taught in this book. Have fun figuring out different ways to repeat the skills taught in this book within your child's daily life.

Point to each airplane and say its color.

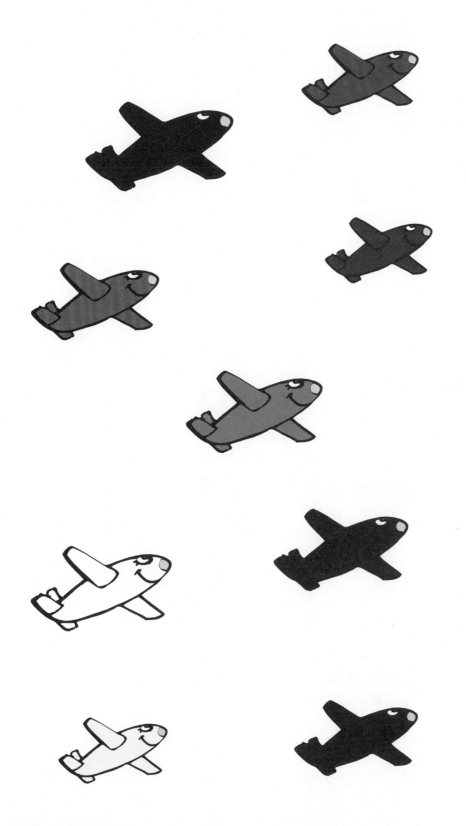

Draw a line segment to connect each hand with the matching numeral.

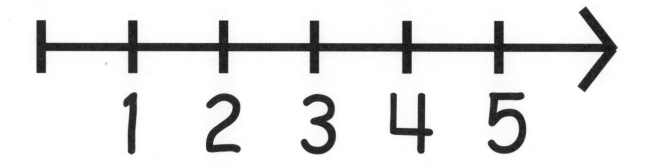

1 2 3 4 5

Draw a line segment to connect each picture with the matching numeral.

1

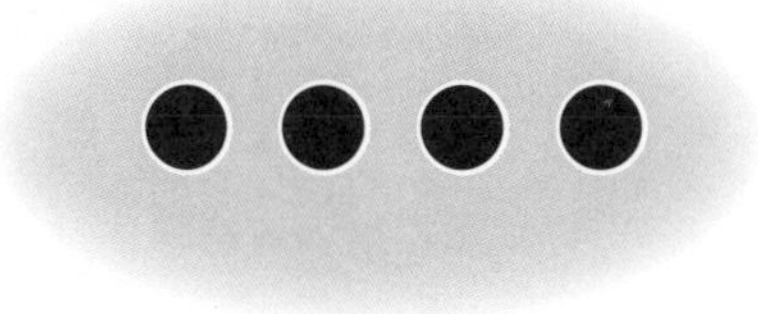

2

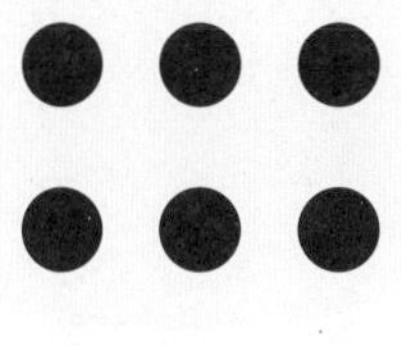

3

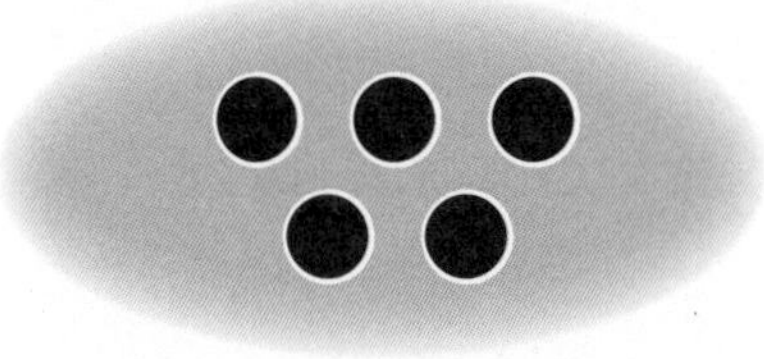

4

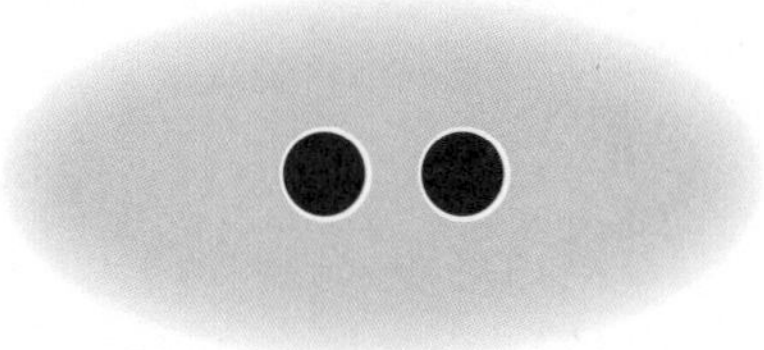

5

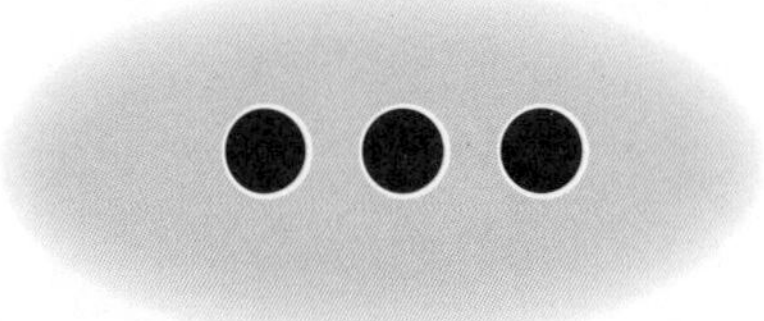

6

Straight Line

Curved Line

Point to the straight line segments.
Point to the curved line segments.

Point to the letters made with straight line segments. Point to the letters made with curved line segments.

A C E F

H I K L

M N O S

T V W X

Y Z

Count the number of footprints in each group.
Draw a line segment to what made the footprints.

Count the six (6) bugs.

Check the groups of 6. ☑

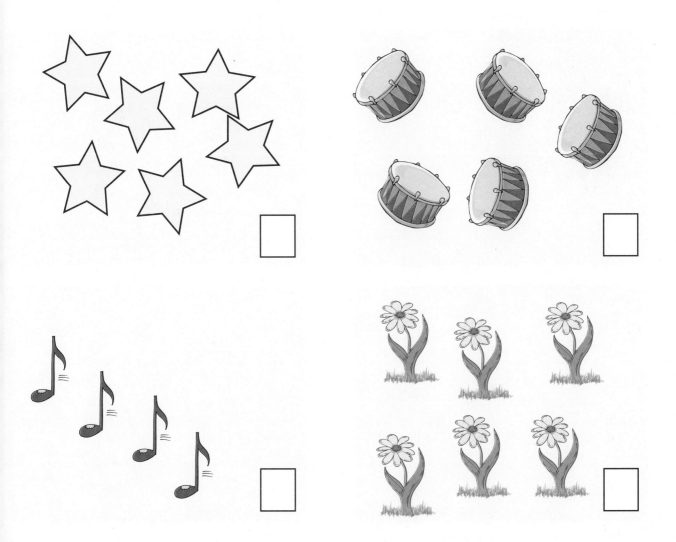

Use the fingers on one hand to show how many objects are in each picture.

Point to the tallest object in each group of pictures.

Count aloud the animals in each picture.

1

4

2

3

5

4

Point to the shorter rectangle in each group of pictures.

Which group shows the bug traveling from the smallest to the largest order?

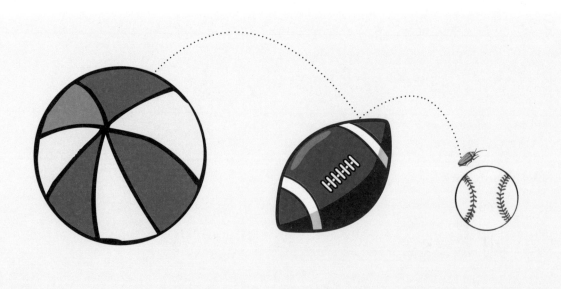

1. How many children are in the picture?

2. How many kites are in the picture?

3. Draw a string from each kite to each child's matching color.

4. Do all the children have kites?

5. How could a child lose a kite?

6. If you lost a kite, would you be happy or sad?

Touch and say the name of each figure in the pattern. Then say the name of the object behind the curtain.

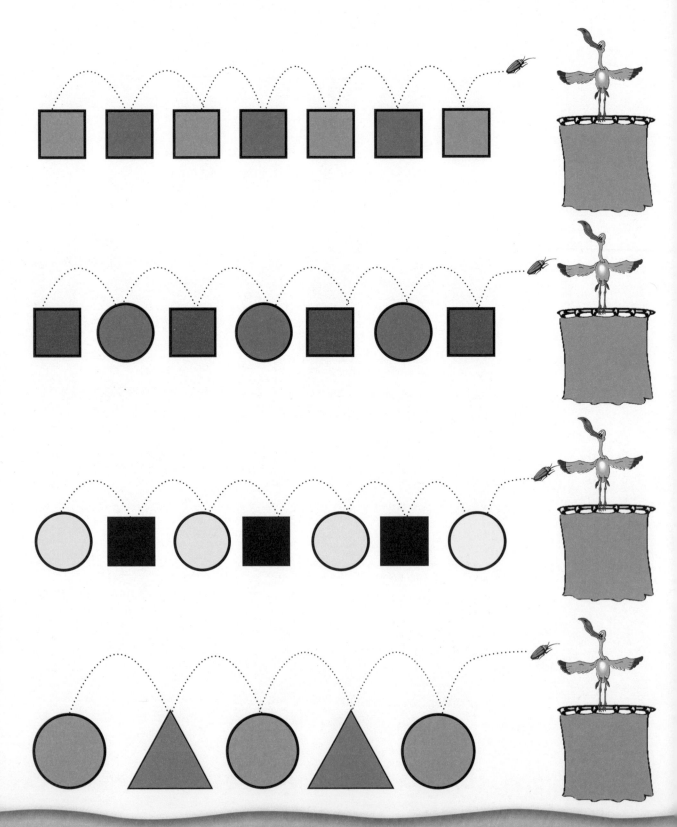

Corners are made when straight line segments meet.

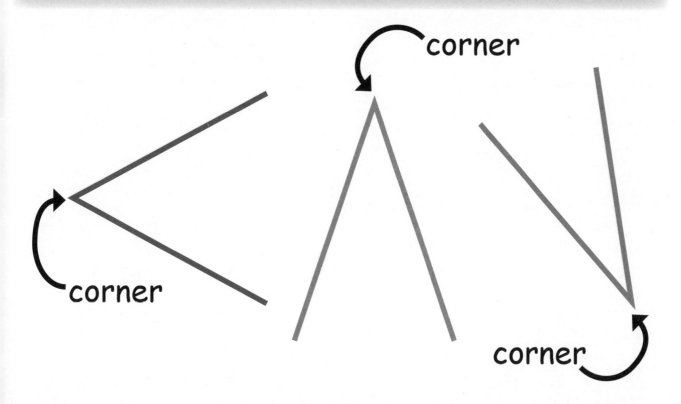

corner

corner

corner

How many corners does this shape have?

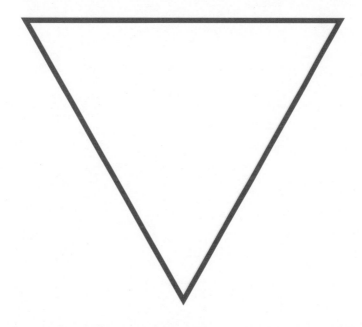

Triangles have 3 sides and 3 corners.

Point to each shape below and say if it is a triangle.

How many straight sides are in a triangle?
How many corners are in a triangle?

Draw a triangle.

Teaching Note: The child should draw only the border. The inside of the triangle should not be colored.

Thinker Doodles™*

1. Look at each face above, then find its unfinished picture below. Use a pencil to draw in all the missing parts.

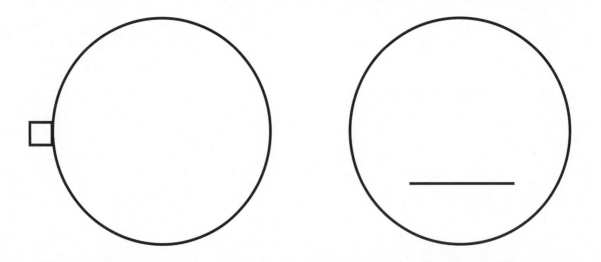

2. Color the happy faces using three colors.

3. Use two colors on the faces with circles for ears.

*For more activities like this, please see our *Thinker Doodles™* series.

Point to the triangle in each row that is not the same size and shape.

Point to the <u>largest</u> triangle and say its color.

Point to the <u>smallest</u> triangle and say its color.

Point to and count aloud the triangles in the picture.

Draw 2 triangles that are the same size and shape.

A rectangle has 4 straight sides and 4 corners.

Point to and count each side of the orange rectangle.
Point to and count each corner of the orange rectangle.

Point to each shape and say if it is a rectangle.

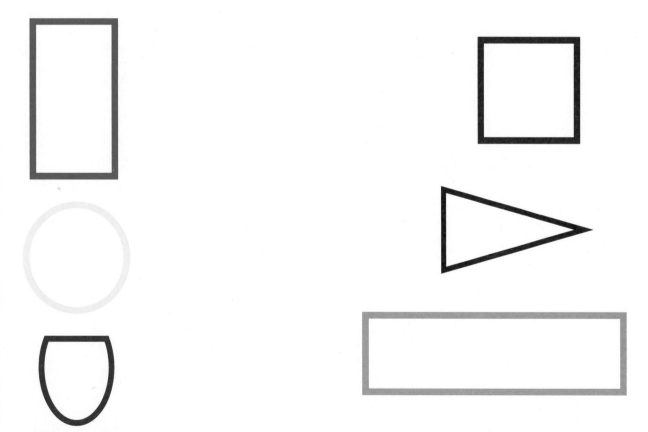

Teaching Note: It is correct if your child responds that the blue square is a rectangle. It has 4 straight sides and 4 corners.

How many straight sides are in a rectangle?
How many corners are in a rectangle?

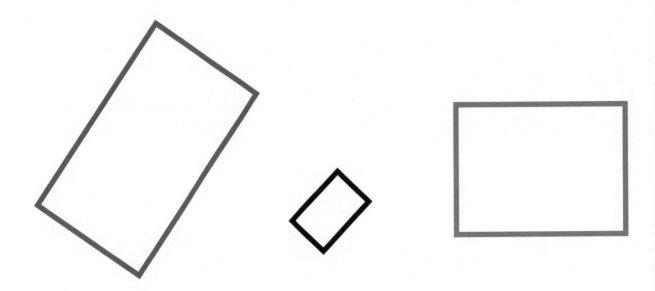

Draw a rectangle.

Teaching Note: Your child should draw only the border. The inside of the rectangle should not be colored.

Point to the rectangle in each row that is not the same size and shape.

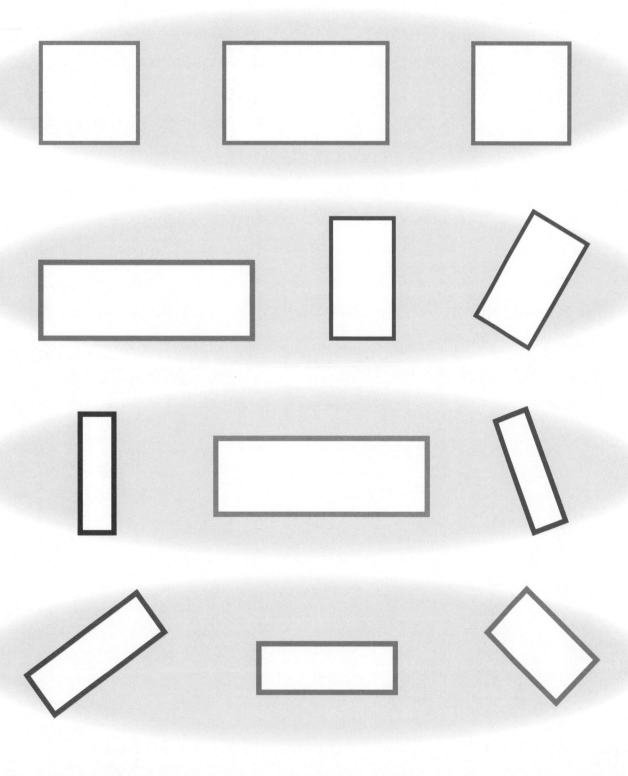

Count aloud the animals in each picture.

The yellow runner is first, the red runner
is second, and the blue runner is third.

Point to the runner who is first.
Point to the runner who is second.
Point to the runner who is third.

Point to and say the color of the first boat.
Point to and say the color of the second boat.
Point to and say the color of the third boat.

Count aloud and point to each picture with five things.

1. How many yellow circles are on the clown's suit?

2. How many red circles are on the clown's suit?

3. How many blue circles are on the clown's suit?

4. How many circles are on the clown's suit?

1. How many yellow crayons are in the picture?

2. How many red crayons are in the picture?

3. How many blue crayons are in the picture?

4. How many crayons are in the picture?

5. If a yellow crayon is lost, how many crayons are in the picture?

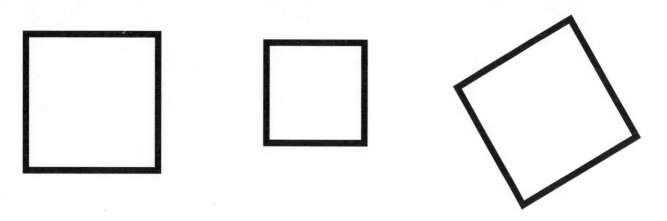

A square is a special type of rectangle.
A square's 4 sides are all the same length.

Point to each shape below and say if it is a square.

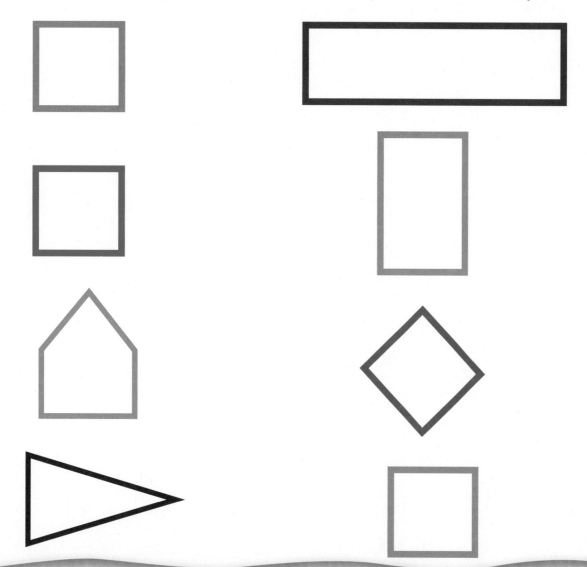

How many straight sides are in a square?
How many corners are in a square?

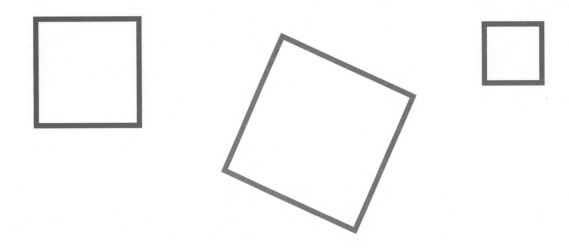

Draw two squares.

Teaching Note: Your child should draw only the border. The inside of the square should not be colored.

1. Point to the picture that has 6 animals in it and say six.

2. Point to the picture that has 5 animals in it and say five.

3. Point to the picture that has the fewest animals in it.

4. Point to the picture that has the most animals in it.

Point to the figure that does not belong.
Divide each group into two groups.
Explain how you made your groups.

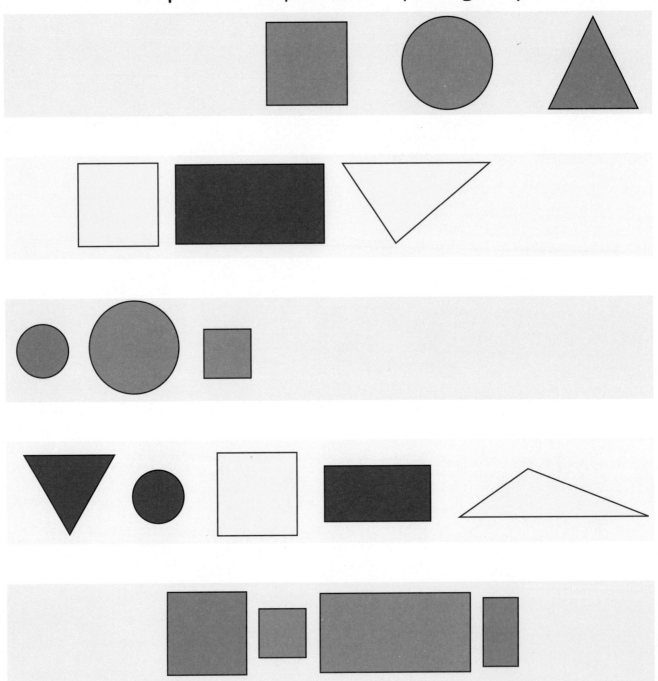

Teaching Note: There is no right answer. Your child could group by color, by shape, by objects that have corners, objects that do not have sharp corners, large and small, and so on. Any rational answer is acceptable provided your child can explain it.

There are no fish in the fishbowl.

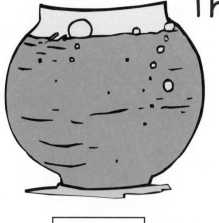

There are 0 fish in the bowl.

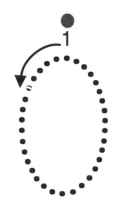

(Trace zero)

0 fish

Put an X on the tree with 0 apples.

Put an X on the dog with 0 spots.

Trace the numeral with your finger.
Start at the red dot. Trace and then
write the numeral with your pencil.
Hold the pencil correctly.

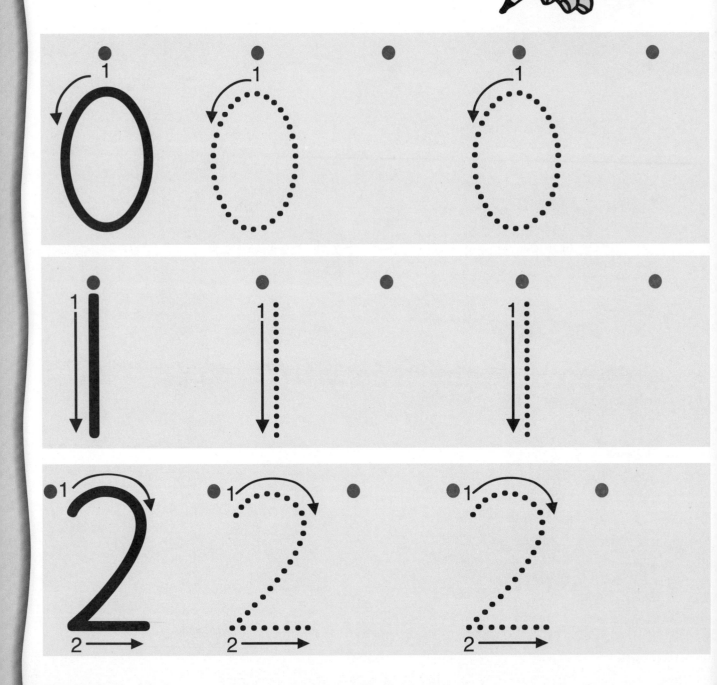

Teaching Note: "Number" is how many. "Numeral" is the written number.

Trace the numeral with your finger. Start at the red dot. Trace and then write the numeral with your pencil. Be sure to hold the pencil correctly.

Teaching Note: "Number" is how many. "Numeral" is the written number. Lift the pencil for step 3 when writing numerals 4 and 5.

Cross out figures in the picture to match the numbers I tell you.

Zero fish

One skunk

2 rabbits

3 dogs

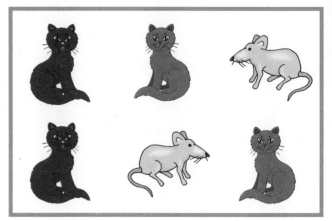

1.   Point to the box with 6 cats.

2.   Point to the box with 4 cats.

3.   Point to the box with the fewest cats.

4.   Point to the box with the most cats.

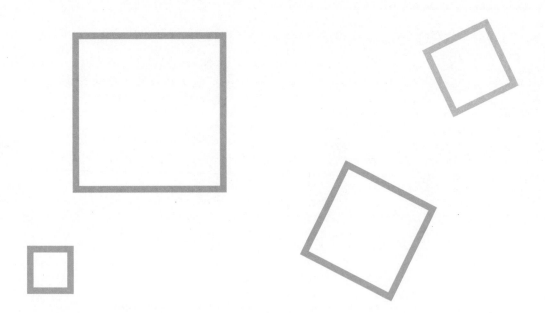

1. Touch each object and say square.

2. Count the number of sides of each square.

3. Count the number of corners of each square.

4. Draw two squares. Do not color the insides.

Touch and say the name of each shape.

Touch and count how many straight sides are in each shape.

Touch and count how many corners are in each shape.

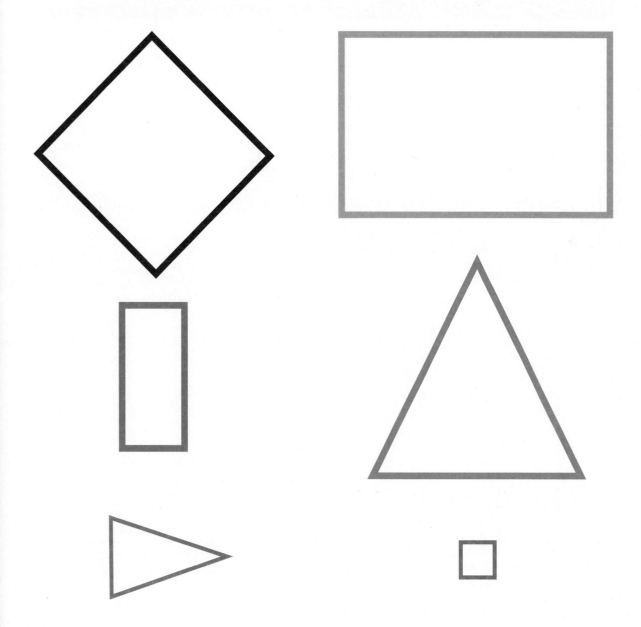

Teaching Note: A square is both a rectangle and a square. If your child calls a square a rectangle, ask him what type of rectangle.

1. Point to the duck that is first in line for breadcrumbs.

2. Point to the duck that is last in line for breadcrumbs.

3. Point to the duck that is third in line for breadcrumbs.

4. Point to the duck that is second in line for breadcrumbs.

Touch and count the bugs.
Touch and say the numbers.

1   2   3   4   5

Which group of balloons is numbered correctly from 1 to 5?

1. Which group is in shortest to longest order?
2. Which group is in longest to shortest order?

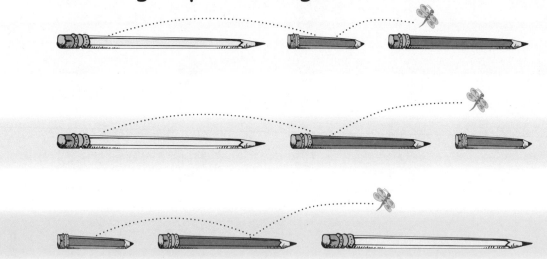

1. Which group is in shortest to tallest order?
2. Which group is in tallest to shortest order?

1. How many children are in the picture?

2. How many balls are in the picture?

3. Draw a line segment from each ball to each child matching their play activity.

4. Does each child have a ball?

Touch the shape and say its name.

1.   Which group is in shortest to longest order?
2.   Which group is in longest to shortest order?

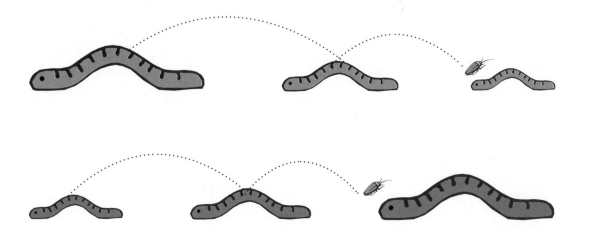

1.   Which group is in shortest to tallest order?
2.   Which group is in tallest to shortest order?

Teaching Note: If necessary, remind your child that the first flower is on the left.

CAN YOU FIND ME?™*

My balloons are not blue.
That is a clue.
If I had two more,
I would have four.

Of the three pictures that you see,
tell me now, can you find me?

*For more activities like this, see our *Can You Find Me?*™ series.

Point to the taller object in each set of pictures.

1. How many brown cows are in the picture?

2. How many white cows are in the picture?

3. How many black cows are in the picture?

4. How many cows are in the picture?

5. Are there more brown cows or black cows in the picture?

6. If you chase one cow away, how many cows are left?

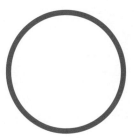  

Point to the shape that matches the description, then say its name.

- the green figure
- the red figure
- the pink figure

- the blue figure
- the black figure
- the brown figure

Teaching Note: A square is both a rectangle and a square. If your child calls a square a rectangle, ask him what type of rectangle.

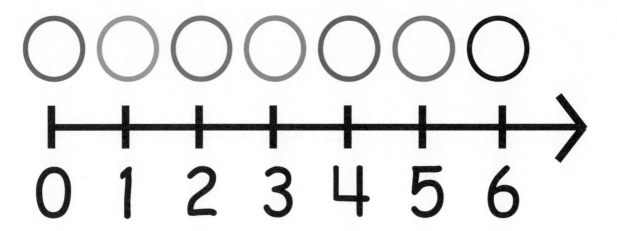

1. Point to the red circle and say the numeral below it.

2. Point to the blue circle and say the numeral below it.

3. Point to the pink circle and say the numeral below it.

4. Point to the purple circle and say the numeral below it.

5. Point to the green circle and say the numeral below it.

6. Point to the orange circle and say the numeral below it.

7. Point to the black circle and say the numeral below it.

1. How many brown dinosaurs are in the picture?

2. How many green dinosaurs are in the picture?

3. How many purple dinosaurs are in the picture?

4. How many dinosaurs are in the picture?

5. Are there more purple or green dinosaurs in the picture?

6. If you chased two dinosaurs away, how many dinosaurs would be left?

Describe the patterns, then continue the patterns.

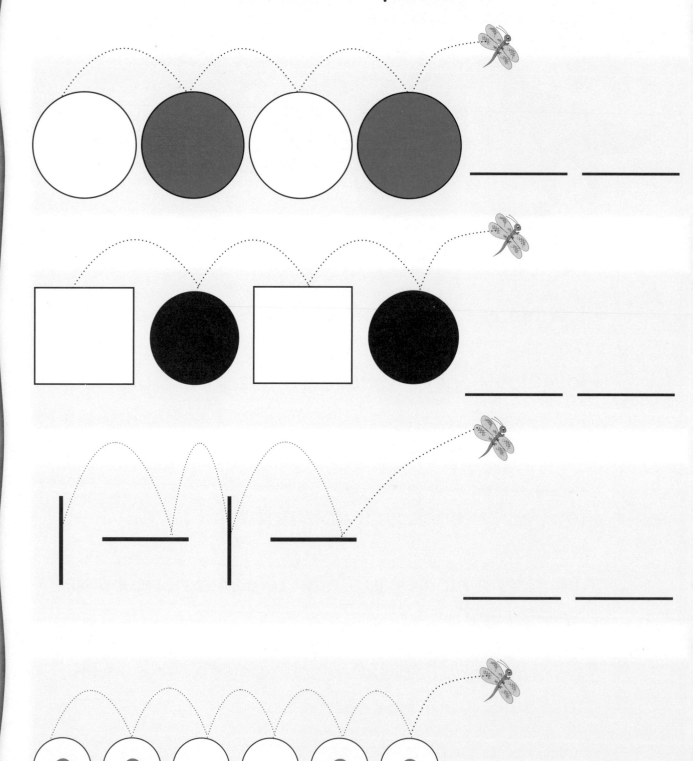

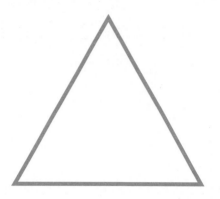

All triangles have 3 sides and three corners.

Point and count aloud the sides of the triangle,
"1, 2, 3."

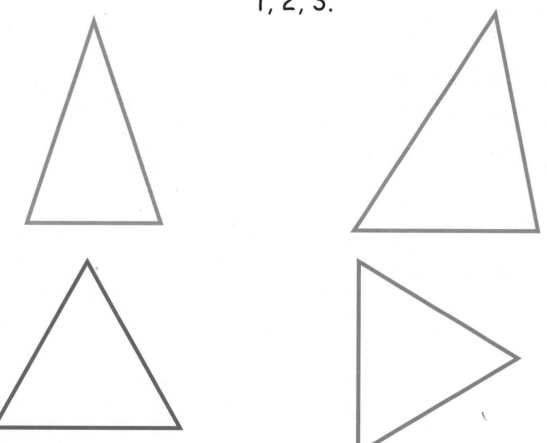

Point and count aloud the three corners
of a triangle.

How many straight sides are in a rectangle?
Touch and count each side of each rectangle.

How many corners are in a rectangle?
Touch and count the corners in each rectangle.

Point to each figure and tell me its shape.

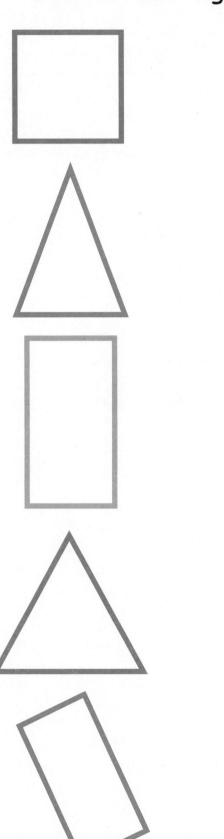

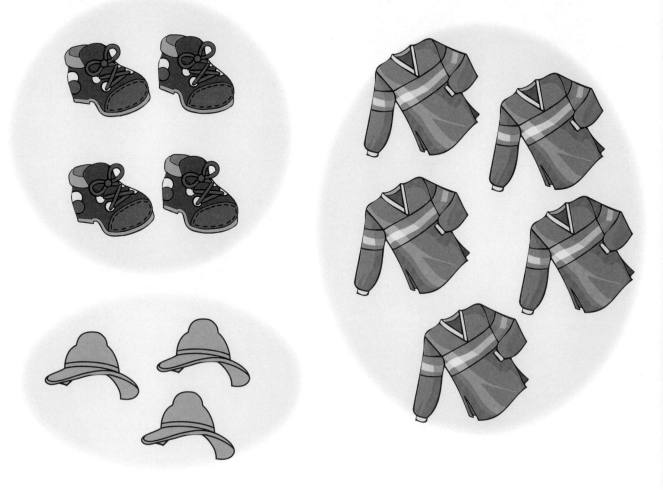

1. Point to the group that has 4 objects in it.

2. Point to the group that has 5 objects in it.

3. Point to the group that has the fewest objects in it.

4. Point to the group that has the most objects in it.

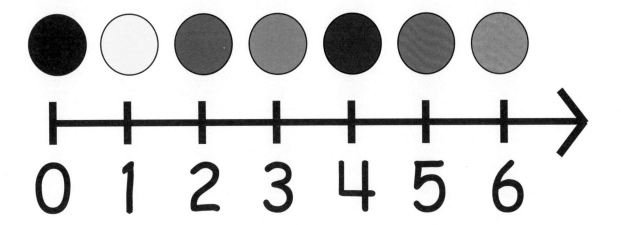

1. Point to the numeral two and say the color above it.

2. Point to the numeral five and say the color above it.

3. Point to the numeral three and say the color above it.

4. Point to the numeral four and say the color above it.

5. Point to the numeral one and say the color above it.

6. Point to the numeral six and say the color above it.

7. Point to the numeral zero and say the color above it.

CAN YOU FIND ME?™*

My pet is long,
but shorter than I.
He has a tail
and one spot you can spy.

Of the three pictures that you can see,
tell me now, can you find me?

*For more activities like this, see our *Can You Find Me?*™ series.

Find each of the shapes in the picture below.

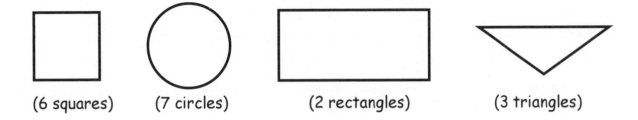

(6 squares)   (7 circles)   (2 rectangles)   (3 triangles)

1 2 3 4 5 6 7

Count seven dots.

Check the groups of 7.

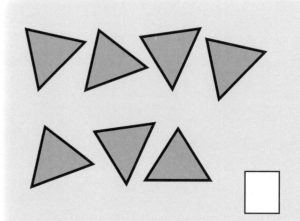

Count eight (8) candies.

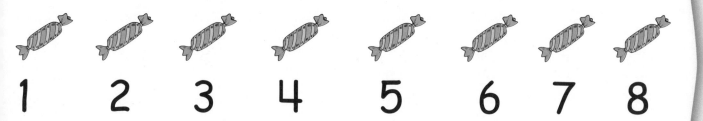

1   2   3   4   5   6   7   8

Check the groups of 8. ✓

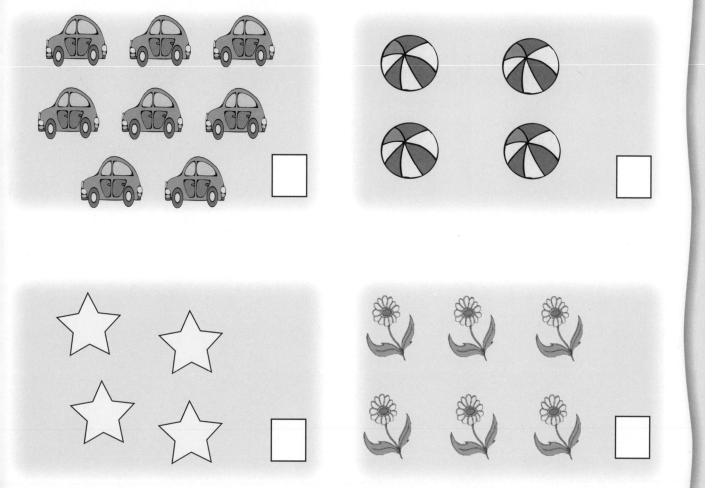

How many balloons are blue?

Color more to make 6 blue balloons.

How many triangles are green?

Color more to make 6 green triangles.

Teaching Note: Encourage your child to color within the lines.

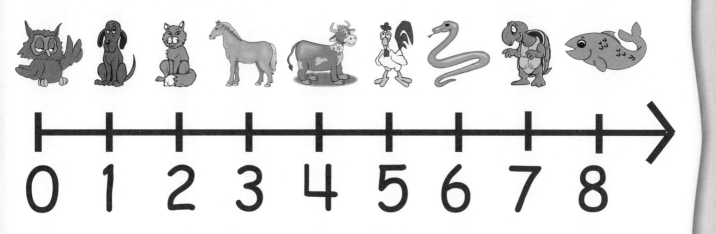

1. Point to the numeral zero and say the animal above it.

2. Point to the numeral two and say the animal above it.

3. Point to the numeral one and say the animal above it.

4. Point to the numeral six and say the animal above it.

5. Point to the numeral five and say the animal above it.

6. Point to the numeral three and say the animal above it.

7. Point to the numeral four and say the animal above it.

8. Point to the numeral seven and say the animal above it.

9. Point to the numeral eight and say the animal above it.

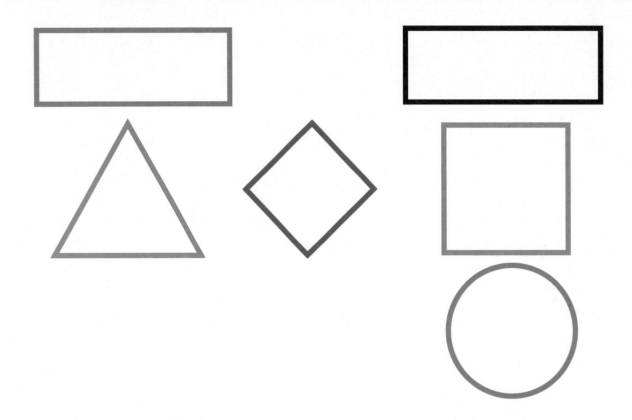

1. Point to the shape directly above the blue triangle.

2. Point to the shape between the triangle and the blue square.

3. Point to the shape between the black rectangle and the circle.

4. Draw an X over the shape directly below the green rectangle.

Which row in each group has more things in it? Explain how you decided.

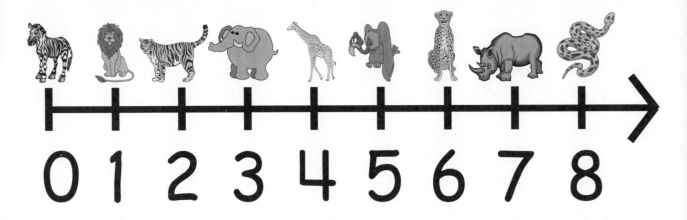

1. Point to the elephant and say the numeral below it.

2. Point to the tiger and say the numeral below it.

3. Point to the vulture and say the numeral below it.

4. Point to the cheetah and say the numeral below it.

5. Point to the giraffe and and say the numeral below it.

6. Point to the lion and say the numeral below it.

7. Point to the zebra and say the numeral below it.

8. Point to the rhino and say the numeral below it.

9. Point to the snake and say the numeral below it.

Bobo

Coco

Jojo

1. Count the boxes each clown is holding.
   Under each clown, write the number of boxes.

2. Which clown is holding the most boxes?_____

3. How many fewer boxes does the blue clown have
   than the green clown? _____

4. How many more boxes does the red clown have
   than the green clown? _____

Draw a line segment from each girl to her toys.

Tammy has only toys with wheels.

Megan has the most toys.

Deb has the least toys.

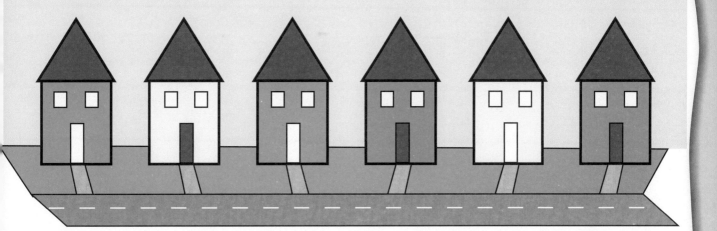

1. How many yellow houses are in the picture?

2. How many green houses are in the picture?

3. How many blue houses are in the picture?

4. How many houses are in the picture?

5. Are there more yellow or blue houses in the picture?

6. If you painted a yellow house blue, how many blue houses would there be?

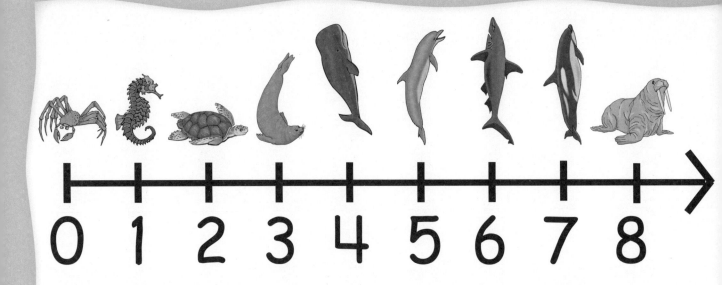

1. Point to the numeral seven and say the name of the animal above it.

2. Point to the numeral zero and say the name of the animal above it.

3. Point to the numeral six and say the name of the animal above it.

4. Point to the numeral five and say the name of the animal above it.

5. Point to the numeral four and say the name of the animal above it.

6. Point to the numeral three and say the name of the animal above it.

7. Point to the numeral two and say the name of the animal above it.

8. Point to the numeral eight and say the name of the animal above it.

Mind Benders®*

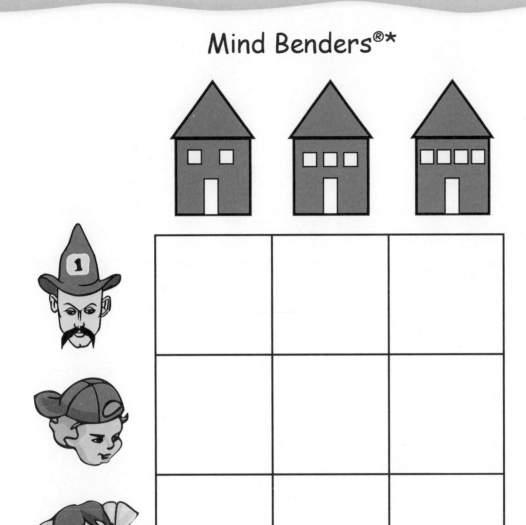

A fireman, a boy, and a girl all live in different houses. Read the clues and fill in the chart using "Y" for yes and "N" for no to solve the puzzle.

1. The fireman's house has less than 3 windows.

2. The boy's house has the most windows.

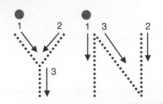

Teaching Note: Teach your child to mark each yes and no answer learned from each clue. The problem is finished when all boxes are marked correctly.

*For more activities like this, please see our *Mind Benders®* series.

1. How many brown bears are in the picture?

2. How many white bears are in the picture?

3. How many gray bears are in the picture?

4. How many black bears are in the picture?

5. How many bears are in the picture?

6. Are there more white bears or brown bears in the picture?

7. If two bears leave, how many bears are left?

There were this many
candies in my pocket.

Then I ate 3 candies.

Put an X over 3 candies.

How many are still inside my pocket? _____

There were this many
pennies inside my bank.

Then I spent 2 pennies.

Put an X over 2 pennies.

How many are still inside the bank? _____

Trace the numeral with your finger. Start at the red dot. Trace and then write the numeral with your pencil. Hold the pencil correctly.

Trace the numeral with your finger. Start at the red dot. Trace and then write the numeral with your pencil. Be sure to hold the pencil correctly.

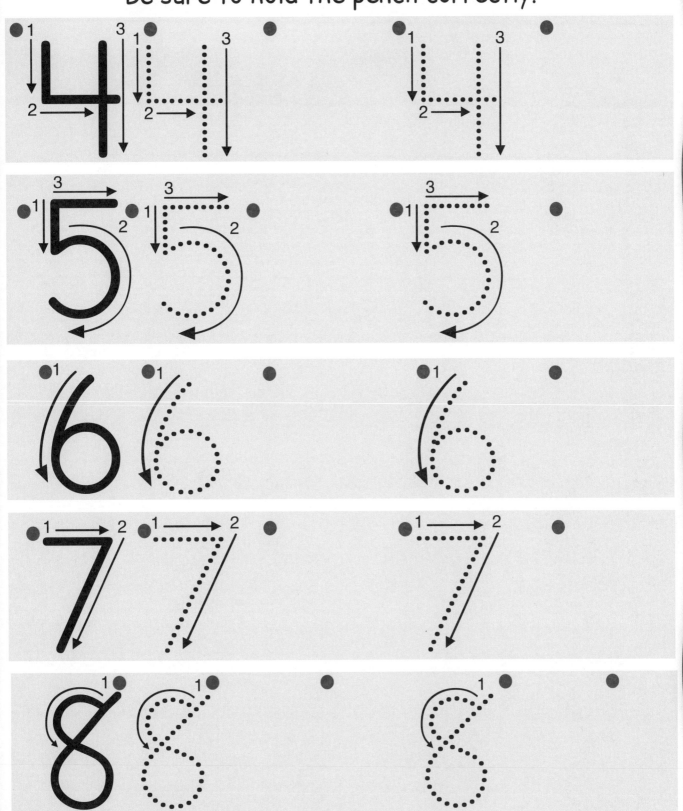

Teaching Note: Lift the pencil for step 3 when writing numerals 4 and 5.

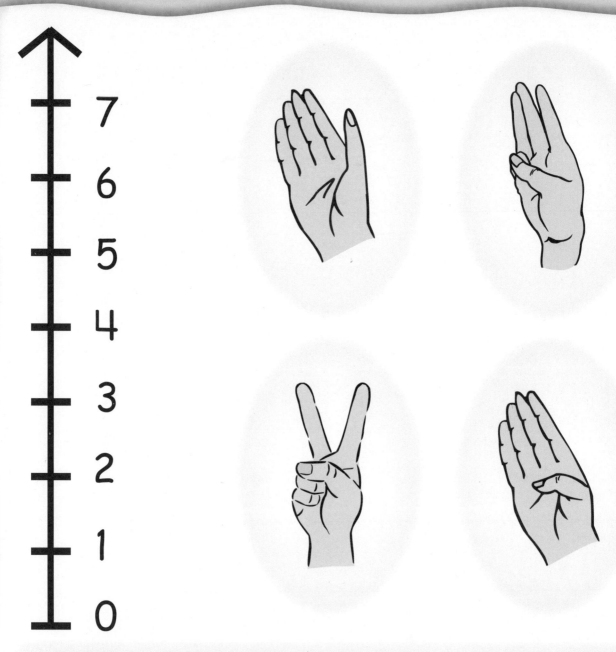

1. Touch the hand holding up five fingers and say 5. Draw a line segment from the hand to the 5 mark on the number line.

2. Touch the hand holding up three fingers and say 3. Draw a line segment from the hand to the 3 mark on the number line.

3. Touch the hand holding up four fingers and say 4. Draw a line segment from the hand to the 4 mark on the number line.

4. Touch the hand holding up two fingers and say 2. Draw a line segment from the hand to the 2 mark on the number line.

Touch the first box and say first.
Touch the second box and say second.
Touch the third box and say third.
Touch the fourth box and say fourth.

Which color is first?
Which color is second?
Which color is third?
Which color is fourth?

1. Point to the picture with the most toys beside the boy.

2. Point to the picture with the least toys in front of the boy.

3. Point to the picture with a toy behind the boy.

Mind Benders®*

Three worms all have different ages (1, 2, 3). Read the clues and fill in the chart using "Y" for yes and "N" for no to solve the puzzle.

1. The longest worm is not the youngest.

2. The shortest worm will be 3 next year.

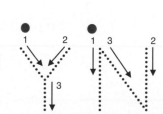

Teaching Note: Teach your child to mark each yes and no answer learned from each clue. The problem is finished when all boxes are marked correctly.

*For more activities like this, please see our *Mind Benders®* series.

1. Point to the picture that has more children playing beside the schoolhouse than in front.

2. Point to the picture with the most children playing in front of the schoolhouse.

3. Point to the picture that has a student flying a kite in back of the schoolhouse.

Point to the rectangle that is longer
in each set (group) and say longer.

Teaching Note: It may be the case that your child might not be able to answer which is longer when the left edges are not aligned.

How many goats are in the picture?
How many sheep are in the picture?
How many animals are in the picture?

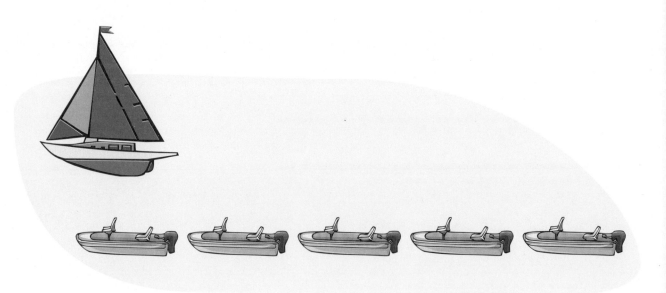

How many sailboats are in the picture?
How many powerboats are in the picture?
How many boats are in the picture?

Mind Benders®*

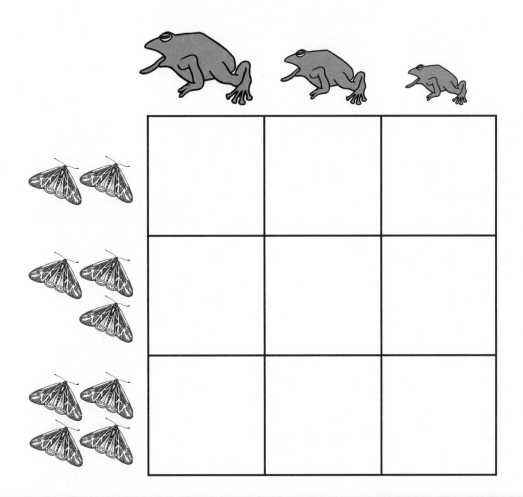

Three frogs all ate moths for dinner. Find out how many moths each frog ate. Read the clues and fill in the chart using "Y" for yes and "N" for no to solve the puzzle.

1. The biggest frog had more than 3 moths.

2. The smallest frog had more than two moths.

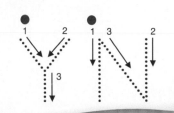

Teaching Note: Teach your child to mark each yes and no answer learned from each clue. The problem is finished when all boxes are marked correctly.

*For more activities like this, please see our *Mind Benders®* series.

These fish bowls contain about the same number of fish.

Which two trees have about the same number of oranges?

Which necklaces have about the same number of beads?

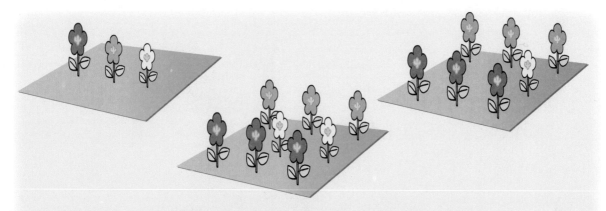

Which gardens have about the same number of flowers?

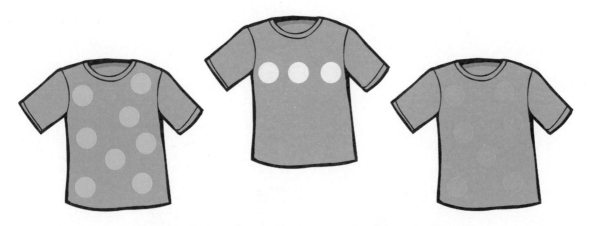

Which shirts have about the same number of dots?

Count how many steps it will take you to go from one side of your bedroom to the other side.

Count how many of your hands it will take to cross the top of your kitchen table.

Count how many pencils it will take to go from one side of your bed to the other side.

Point to the group that has six things.

Point to the group that has six things.

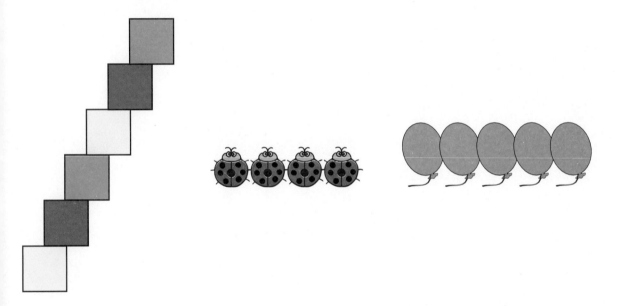

Point to the group that has six things.

 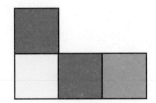 

Cross out animals to make the pictures match the numerals.

2

3

4

5

How many hats are in the picture?

How many coats are in the picture?

How many pieces of clothing are in the picture?

How many owls are in the picture?

How many rabbits are in the picture?

How many animals are in the picture?

1. How many baseball gloves does the coach have?

2. What color are the pants of the player fourth in line?

3. What color are the pants of the player fifth in line?

4. What color are the pants of the player third in line?

5. What color are the pants of the player second in line?

6. Will every player receive a glove?

1. Point to the picture that has the most dogs beside the dog house.

2. Point to the picture that has the most dogs in front of the dog house.

3. Point to the picture that has a dog in back of the dog house.

Connect the dots by counting from 1 to 7.

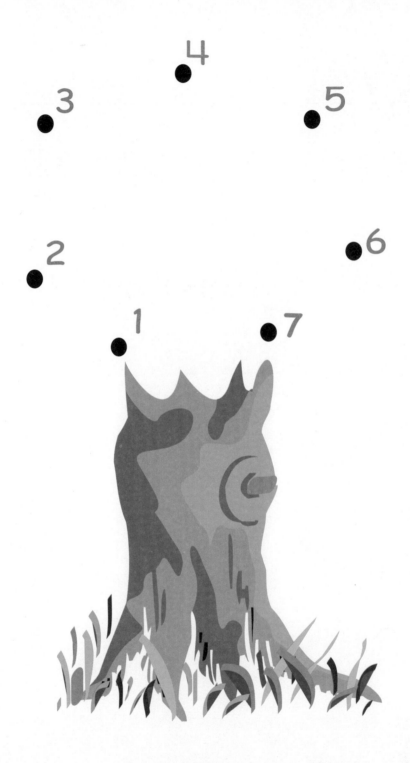

Draw 7 red apples on this tree.

Which two rock piles have about the same number of rocks?

Which two ant hills have about the same number of ants?

Tell how you would use color or shape to split each group into two groups.

Teaching Note: There is no right answer. Any classification that can be rationally explained is acceptable. For example, classify the first group by color. This encourages communication, a fundamental tool in the study of mathematics.

How many squares?

Draw more squares to make 7 squares.

How many circles?

Draw more circles to make 7 circles.

Touch and say the name of each item in the pattern. Then say the name of the object behind the blue curtains.

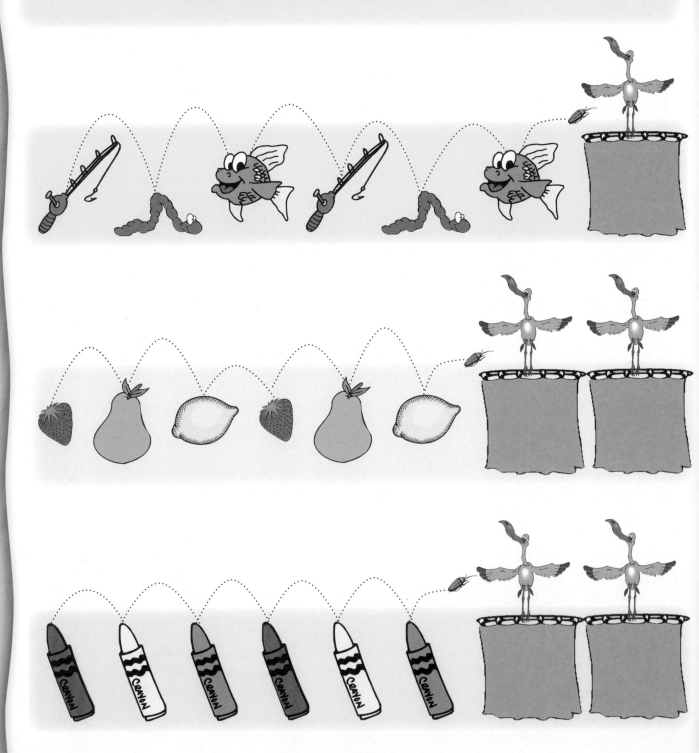

Donald's birthday cake looks like this.

1. How old is Donald?_____

2. How old will he be on his next birthday?_____

Today is Maria's birthday. Last year her birthday cake looked like this.

1. How old was Maria last year? _____
2. How old is she this year?_____
3. How old will she be next year?_____

4 5 6 7 8

How many goats are in the picture?
How many sheep are in the picture?
How many animals are in the picture?

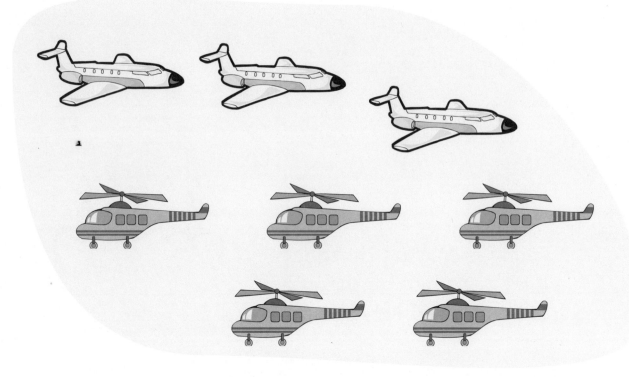

How many jets are in the picture?
How many helicopters are in the picture?
How many aircraft are in the picture?

Touch and say the name of each item in the pattern. Then say the name of the object behind the blue curtains.

Count nine (9) birds.

1 2 3 4 5 6 7 8 9

Check the groups of 9. ☑

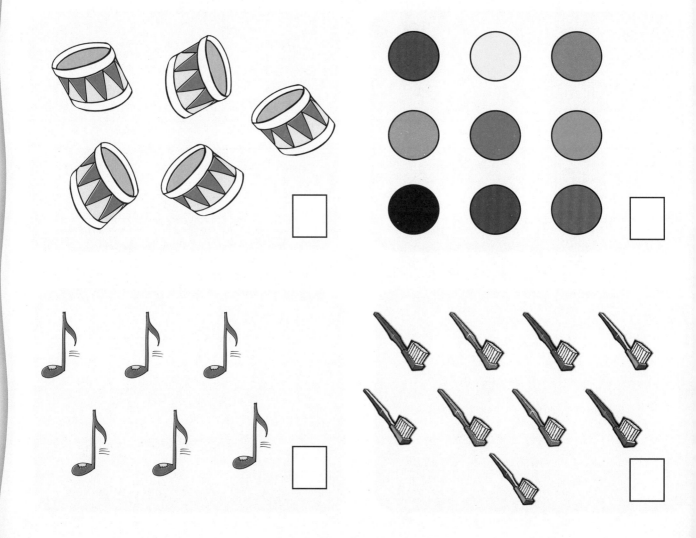

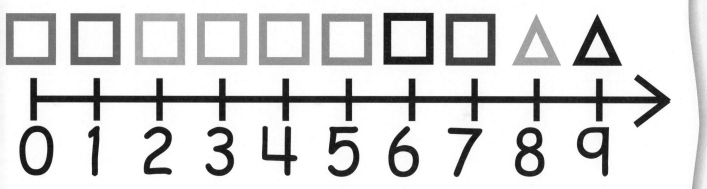

1. Point to the red square and say the numeral below it.

2. Point to the orange square and say the numeral below it.

3. Point to the green square and say the numeral below it.

4. Point to the blue triangle and say the numeral below it.

5. Point to the blue square and say the numeral below it.

6. Point to the purple square and say the numeral below it.

7. Point to the black square and say the numeral below it.

8. Point to the gray square and say the numeral below it.

9. Point to the black triangle and say the numeral below it.

10. Point to the pink square and say the numeral below it.

How many rectangles are in the picture?
Point to and say the color of each rectangle.

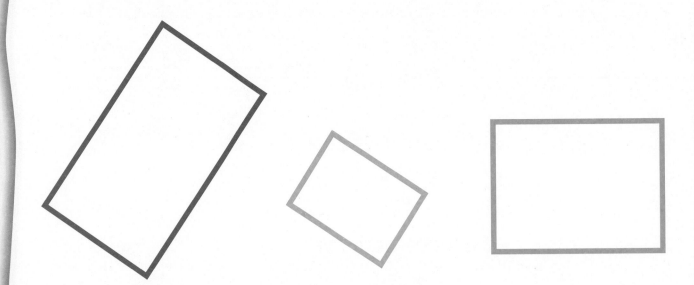

Draw a rectangle and color the inside.

How many cars are being pulled by the engine?

How many blue cars are in the picture?

How many black cars are in the picture?

How many orange cars are in the picture?

If the last train car is removed, how many train cars is the train engine pulling?

How many stars are in the picture? What color are the stars?

How many circles are in the picture? What color are the circles?

How many triangles and squares are in the picture? What colors are they?

Point to and count all 7 shapes in the picture.

How many triangles are in the picture?
Point to and say the color of each triangle.

Draw and color a triangle.

1. Point to and say the shape and color above the numeral 2.

2. Point to and say the shape and color above the numeral 5.

3. Point to and say the shape and color above the numeral 3.

4. Point to and say the shape and color above the numeral 7.

5. Point to and say the shape and color above the numeral 8.

6. Point to and say the shape and color above the numeral 4.

7. Point to and say the shape and color above the numeral 1.

8. Point to and say the shape and color above the numeral 6.

9. Point to and say the shape and color above the numeral 0.

10. Point to and say the shape and color above the numeral 9.

Point to and count the red rectangles.

Point to and count the green rectangles.

Point to and count all the rectangles in the bedroom.

Draw 2 rectangles that are the same size and shape.

Draw a line segment from each figure
to its group below.

Then count the number of objects
that belong to each group.

Trace the numeral with your finger. Start at the red dot. Trace and then write the numeral with your pencil.   Be sure to hold the pencil correctly.

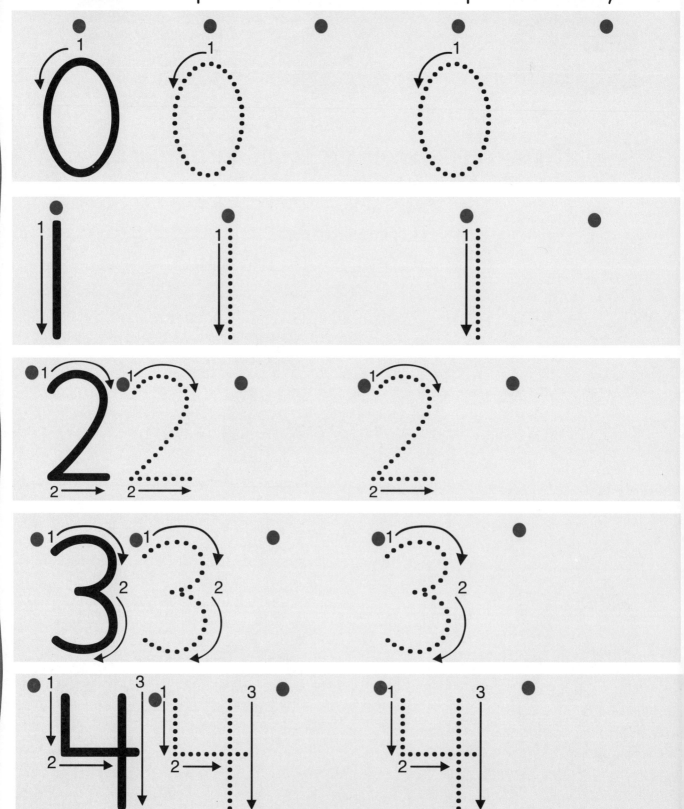

Teaching Note: Lift the pencil for step 3 when writing numerals 4 and 5.

Trace the numeral with your finger. Start at the red dot. Trace and then write the numeral with your pencil. Be sure to hold the pencil correctly.

Teaching Note: Lift the pencil for step 3 when writing numerals 4 and 5.

1. How many brushes have red paint on them in the picture?

2. How many brushes have yellow paint on them in the picture?

3. How many brushes have green paint on them in the picture?

4. Which two colors have the same number of brushes?

Trace the numerals, then write the number of dots in each group.

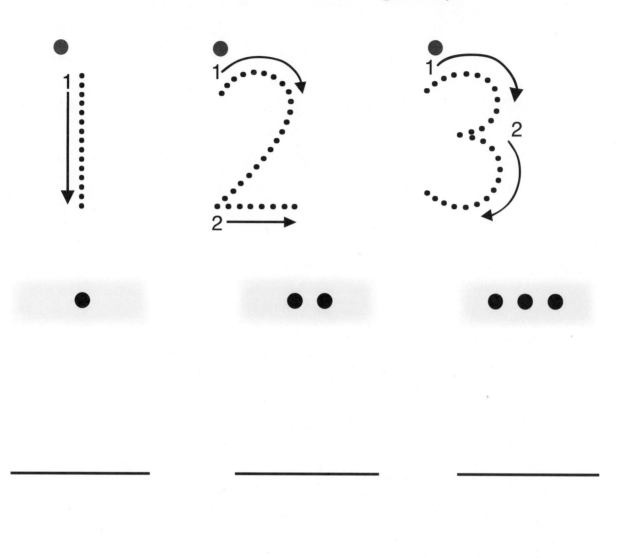

Trace the numerals, then write the number of dots in each group.

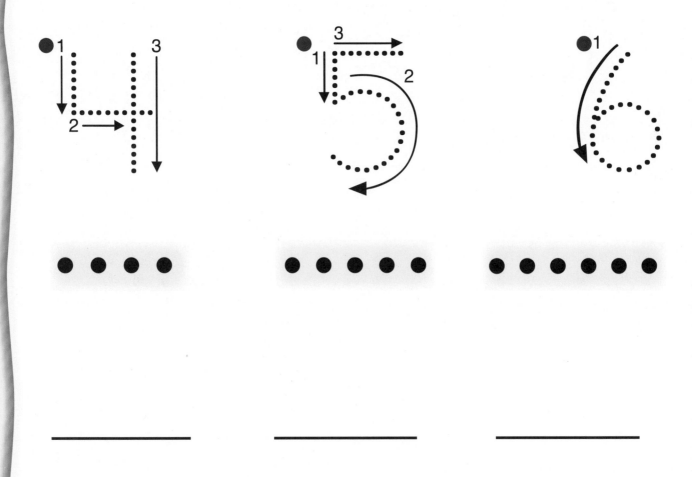

_____   _____   _____

_____   _____   _____

Teaching Note: Lift the pencil for step 3 when writing numerals 4 and 5.

Trace the numerals, then write the number of dots in each group.

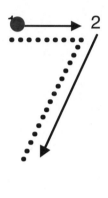

_____

_____

_____

_____

_____

_____

1. Point to the picture with all the cupcakes in front of the bear.

2. Point to the picture with all the cupcakes beside the bear.

3. Point to the picture with the most cupcakes beside the bear.

4. Which bear could eat three cupcakes in front of him?

Some fish in the tank are **red**, some are yellow, and some are **red** and yellow.

1. Without counting, circle the color of fish you think there are the **most** of.

2. Write or say how many of each color of fish are in the tank. Write the number of each color on the line.

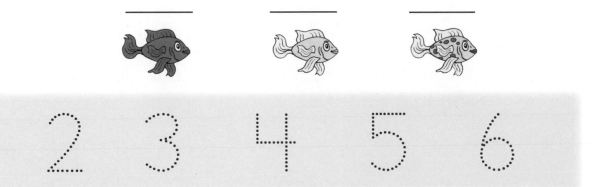

Point to the faster object in each set of pictures.

Draw a line segment from each figure to its group.
Then count aloud the number of objects that belong to each group.

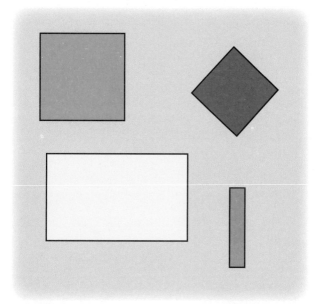

Cross out animals to make the picture match the numeral below it.

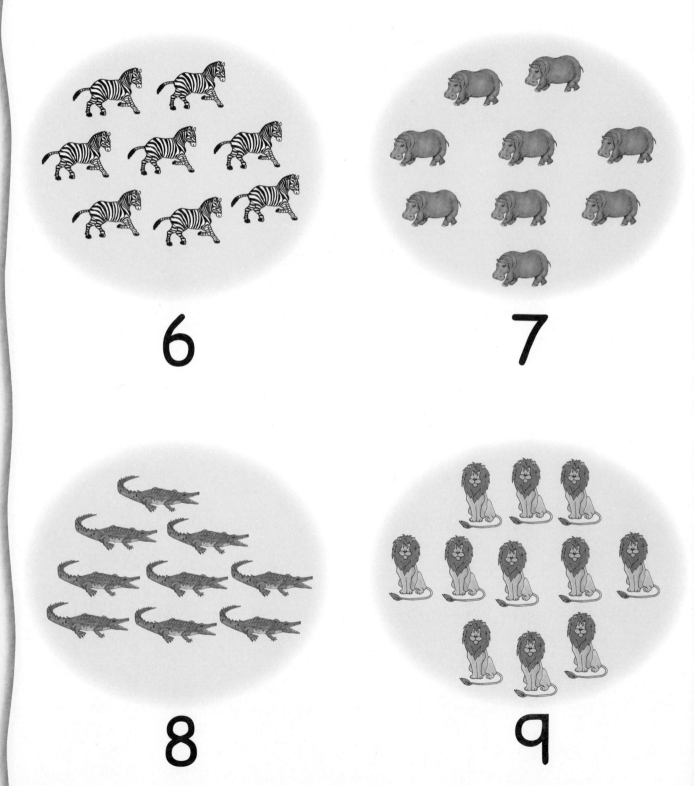

6

7

8

9

1. Some flowers are in the vase. How many?

2. How many flowers are outside the vase?

3. Is the man outside or inside the house?

4. Is the cat outside or inside the house?

5. Is the clock above or below the window?

6. Is the cat above or below the table?

7. Is the book on or in the table?

How many triangles
are in the picture?

What color are the
girl's shoes?

What colors are the
girl's dress?

What color is the
girl's hair?

0 1 2 3 4 5 6 7 8 9

Draw and color a picture using as many
triangles as you can.

1. In each group, point to the column that has more in it.

2. In each group, point to the column that has less in it.

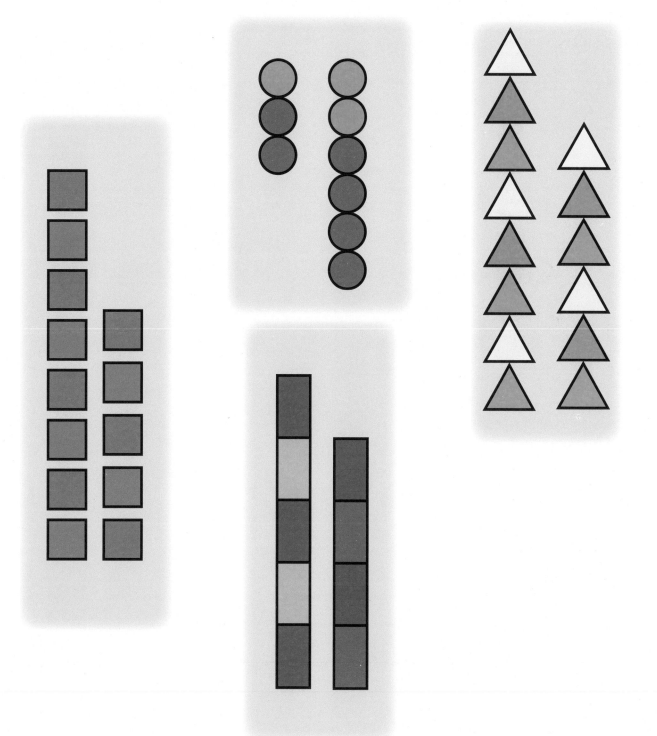

Steven likes to share by giving away half of each type of food in his lunch box. Draw a circle around the food Steven will give to his friends.

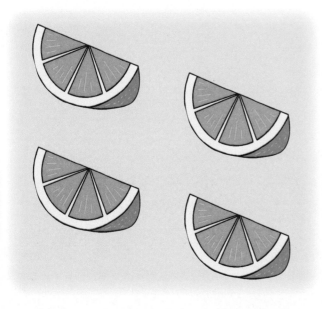

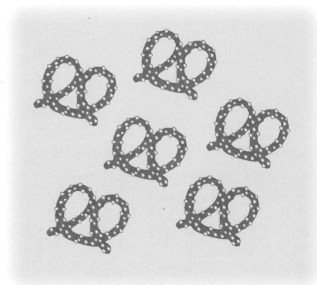

Are there more books beside or in front of the boy?

Are there more books beside or in front of the boy?

How many books are beside and in front of the boy?

Left ⟷ Right

1. Is the black square on the boy's right or left?

2. Is the blue circle on the boy's right or left?

3. Is the red circle on the boy's right or left?

4. What are the colors and shapes of the figures on the boy's left?

Say the number of objects in each box.
Write the number of objects in each box.

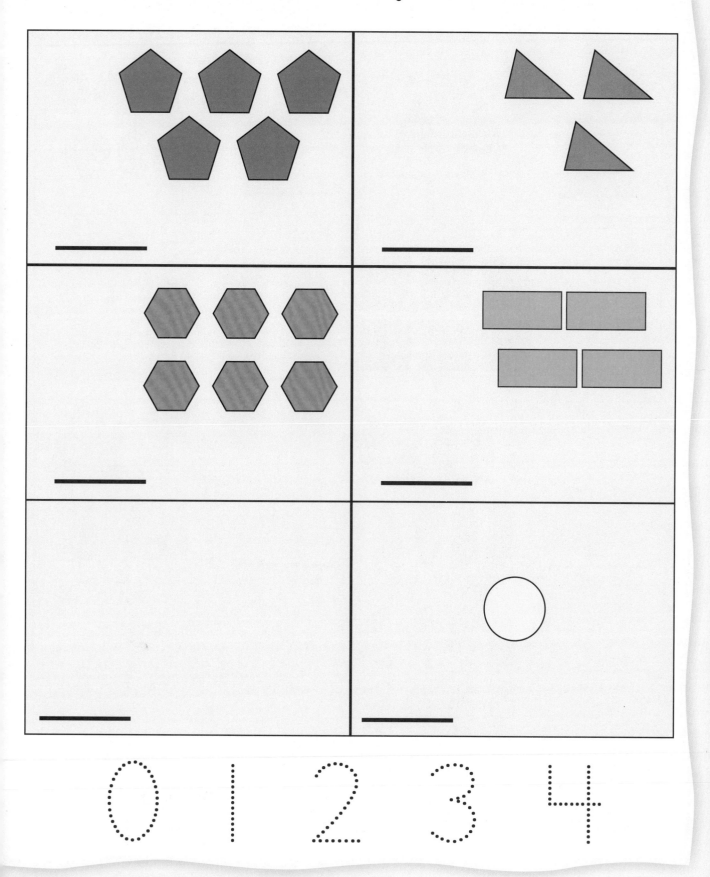

Say the number of objects in each box.
Write the number of objects in each box.

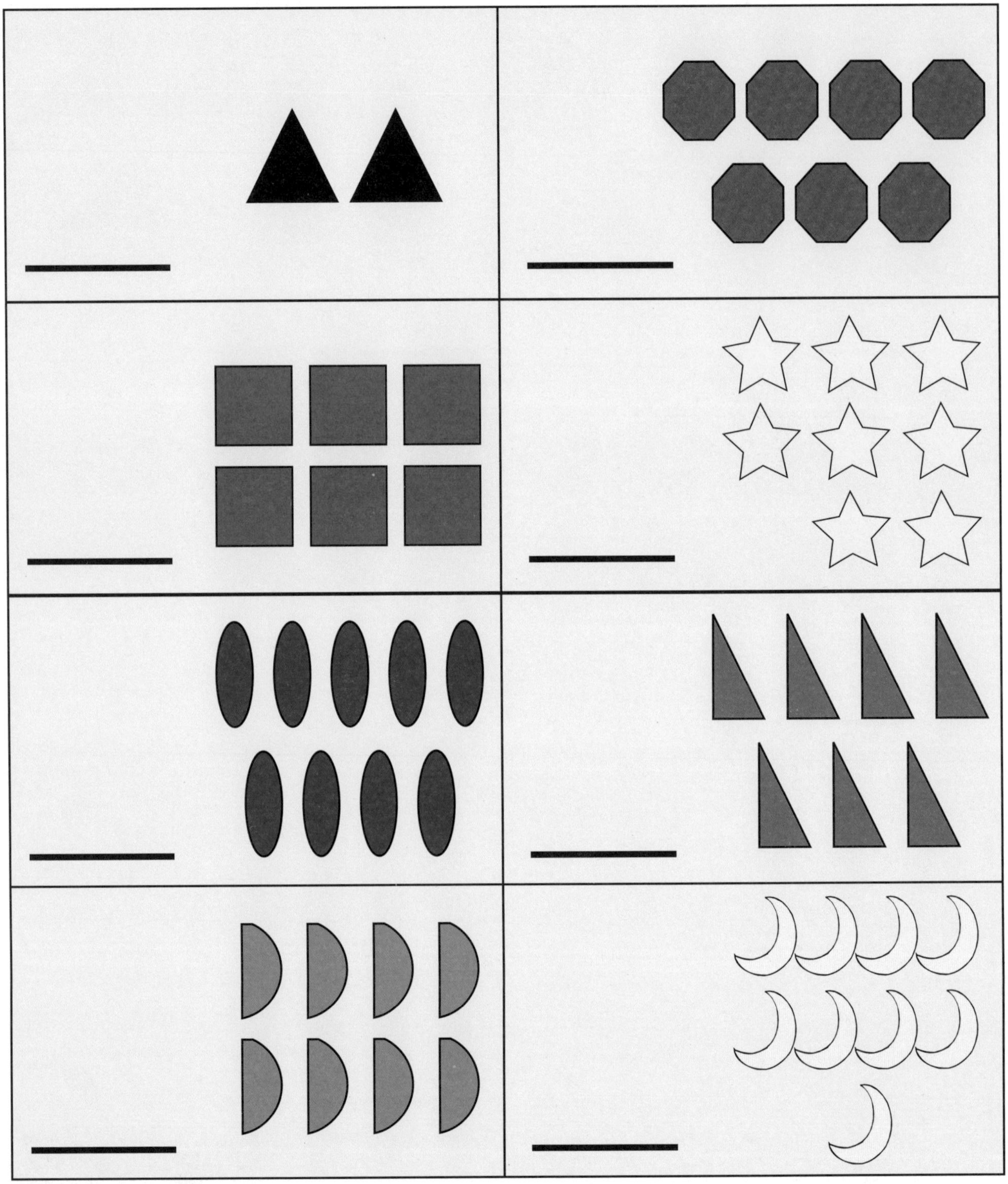

_____

_____

_____

_____

_____

_____

_____

_____

5 6 7 8 9

Touch each shape and say its name.

Teaching Note: A square is both a rectangle and a square. If your child calls a square a rectangle, ask him what type of rectangle.

1. How many straight sides are in a rectangle?
   Touch and count each side of each rectangle.

2. How many corners are in a rectangle? Touch and
   say the number of corners in a rectangle.

3. Draw two rectangles that are the same size and
   shape.

1. How many swings are in the picture?

2. How many children are in the picture?

3. Draw a line segment between each child and a swing.

4. Is there a child not connected with a swing?

5. Is there a swing not connected with a child?

Point to the object that is shorter in each set.

Teaching Note: It may be the case that your child may not be able to answer which is shorter when the left edges are not aligned.

Name the shapes in each set. Point to the two shapes that are the same color, size, and shape in each set.

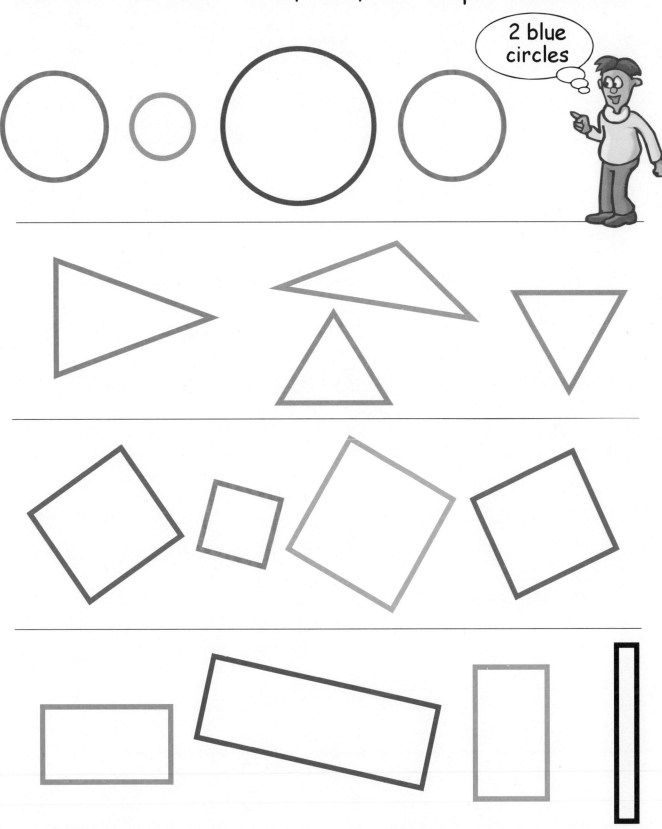

Teaching Note: A square is both a rectangle and a square. If your child calls a square a rectangle, ask him what type of rectangle.

1. What numeral is above the triangle?

2. What numeral is above the green square?

3. What numeral is above the blue circle?

4. What numeral is above the red arrow?

5. What numeral is above the black star?

6. What numeral is above the purple rectangle?

7. What numeral is above the orange square?

8. What numeral is above the black circle?

9. What numeral is above the green star?

10. What numeral is above the blue arrow?

CAN YOU FIND ME?™*

Ted is the tallest.
Lee is the smallest.
I have red hair,
When it is bare

Of the four pictures that you can see,
tell me now, can you find me?

*For more activities like this, see our *Can You Find Me?*™ series.

How many owls are in the picture?
How many chickens are in the picture?
How many birds are in the picture?

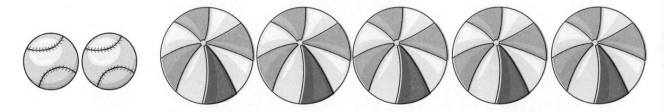

How many baseballs are in the picture?
How many beach balls are in the picture?
How many balls are in the picture?

How many green forks are in the picture?
How many blue forks are in the picture?
How many forks are in the picture?

Half 'n Half Animals™*

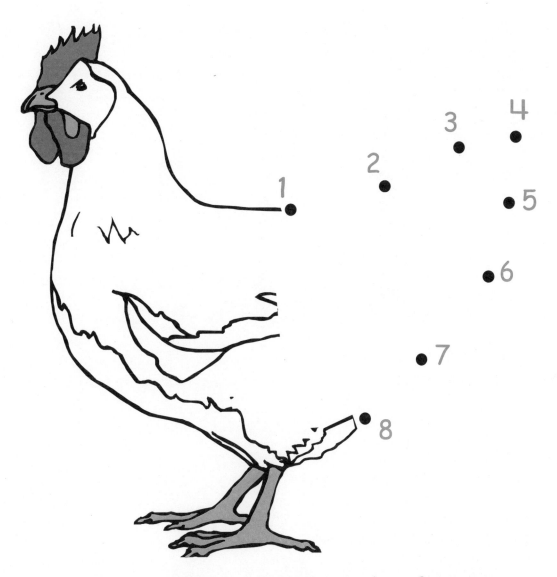

I lay eggs on a nest made of straw.

Connect the dots from 1 to 8, then color the picture. Can you add something else to the picture?

*For more activities like this, please see our *Half 'n Half Animals*™ series.

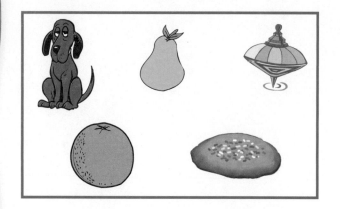

Point to each answer.

1. Which box has eight things?

2. Which box has five things?

3. Which box has six things?

4. Which box has the fewest things?

5. Which box has the most things?

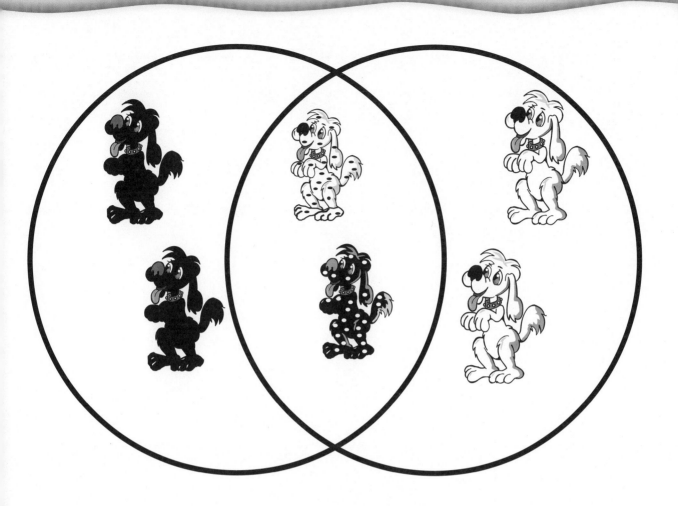

1. How many dogs are there in the picture? _____

2. How many dogs are all black? _____

3. How many dogs are all white? _____

4. How many dogs are both black and white? _____

5. Point to where this dog should go.

2 3 4 5 6 7

Finish coloring the boxes on the graph to show how many children ate each type of ice cream cone.

2 children liked chocolate

3 children liked strawberry

6 children liked vanilla

1. Put an X on the flavor that was the favorite.

2. Circle the kind that was the least favorite.

Lots of bugs came to the picnic. Count how many bugs are in each group and write the total.

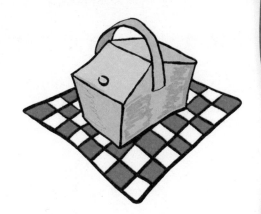

+ =
___

+ =
___

+ =
___

4 5 6 7 8

Count how many bugs are in each group and write the total.

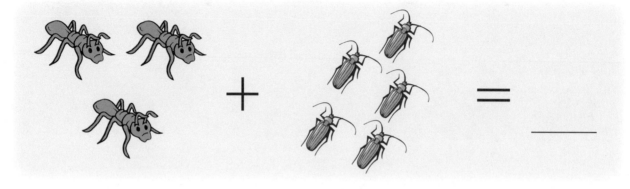

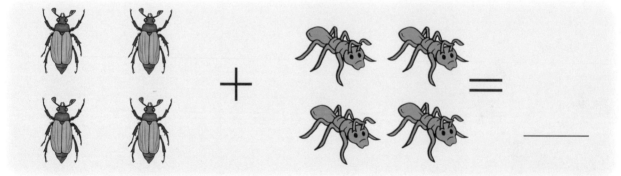

4   5   6   7   8

How many red squirrels are in the picture?

How many gray squirrels are in the picture?

How many squirrels are in the picture?

How many toy bears are in the picture?

How many toy soldiers are in the picture?

How many toys are in the picture?

How many red airplanes are in the picture?

How many blue airplanes are in the picture?

How many airplanes are in the picture?

Tom bought these candies.

1. How many candies did he buy?   _____

He ate this many of them.

Cross this many candies out above to find out how many Tom had left.

2. How many candies did Tom have left?   _____

Ann and Ben bought these cookies at the bake sale.

1. How many cookies
   did they buy?   _____

Cross out the cookies Ann ate.

Cross out the cookies Ben ate.

2. How many cookies were left?   _____

3. Who ate more cookies?   Ben   or   Ann

Use the number line to point to the number of figures in each picture.

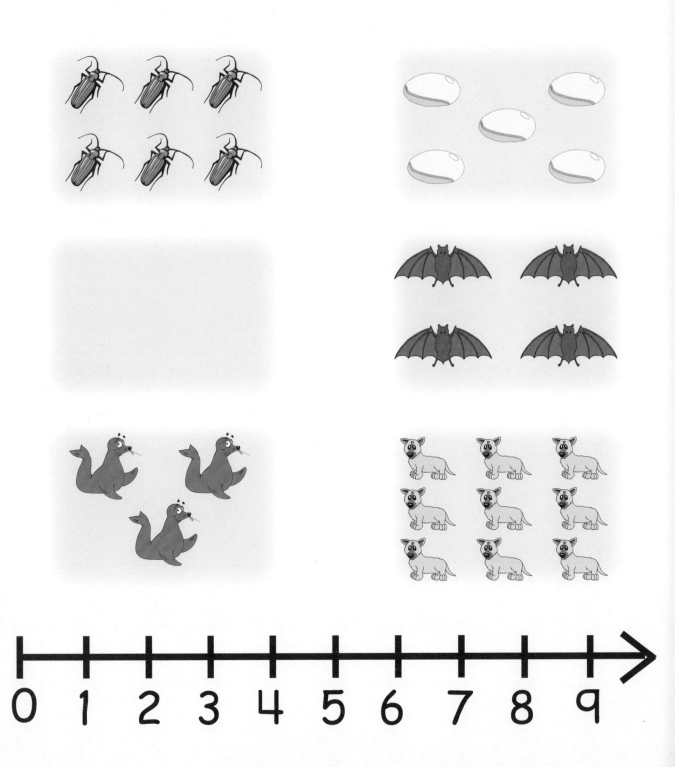

1. How many children are in the picture?

2. How many bicycles are in the picture?

3. Draw a line segment between each bicycle and each child.

4. Are there more children or bicycles?

Cross out animals to make the picture match the numeral below it.

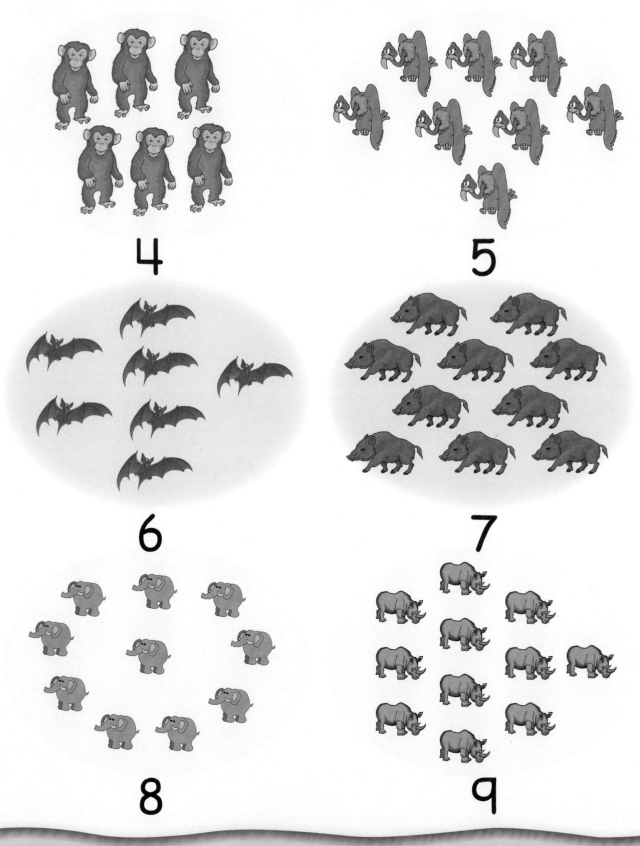

Draw more objects so that each group has 7.

Name the shape used in each group of 7.

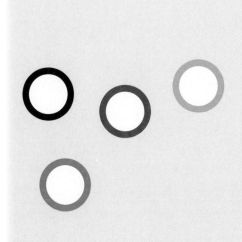

Thinker Doodles™*

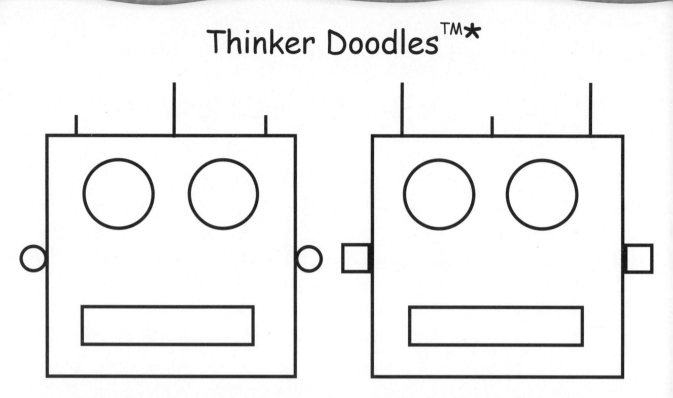

1. Look at each face above, then find its unfinished picture below. Use a pencil to draw in all the missing parts.

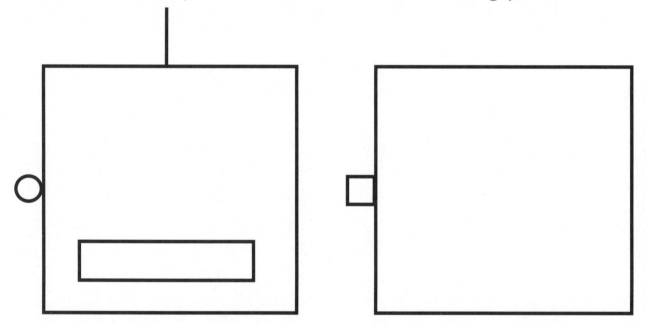

2. Color the faces with 4 circles using 4 colors.
3. Color the faces with 2 long hairs using 2 colors.

*For more activities like this, please see our Thinker Doodles™ series.

How many shirts are blue?

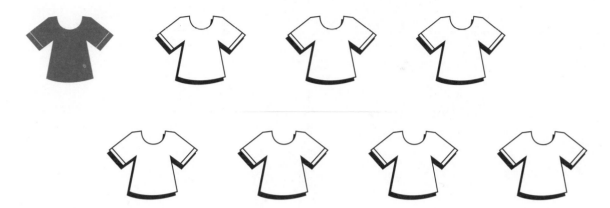

Color more to make 8 blue shirts.

How many books are red?

Color more to make 8 red books.

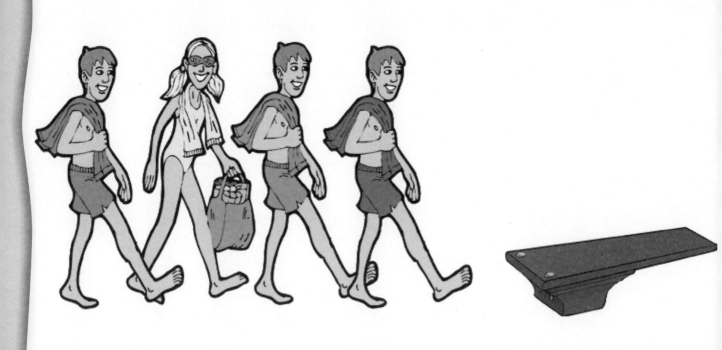

1. Point to the person who is second in line and say the color of his swimsuit.

2. Point to the person who is first in line and say the color of his swimsuit.

3. Point to the person who is fourth in line and say the color of his swimsuit.

4. Point to the person who is third in line and say the color of her swimsuit.

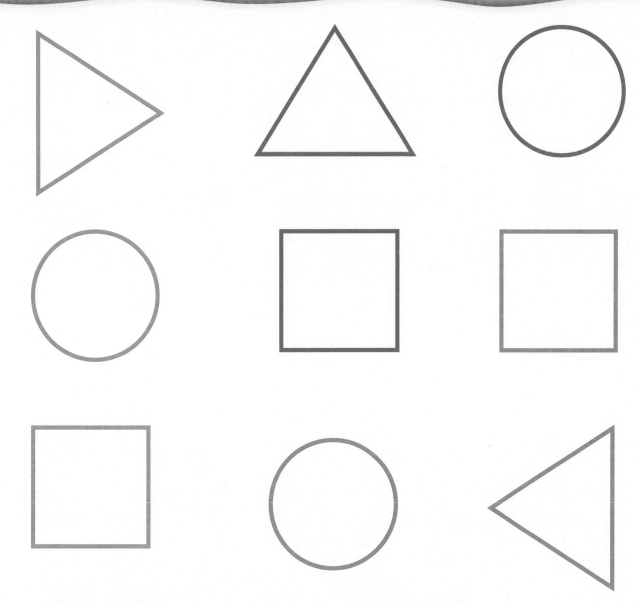

1. What is the color of the circle below the red square?

2. What is the color of the triangle to the right of the green circle?

3. What is the color of the triangle to the left of the red triangle?

4. What is the color of the circle above the green square?

Which flower does not belong with the row of flowers? Explain why it does not belong.

Find each shape below.

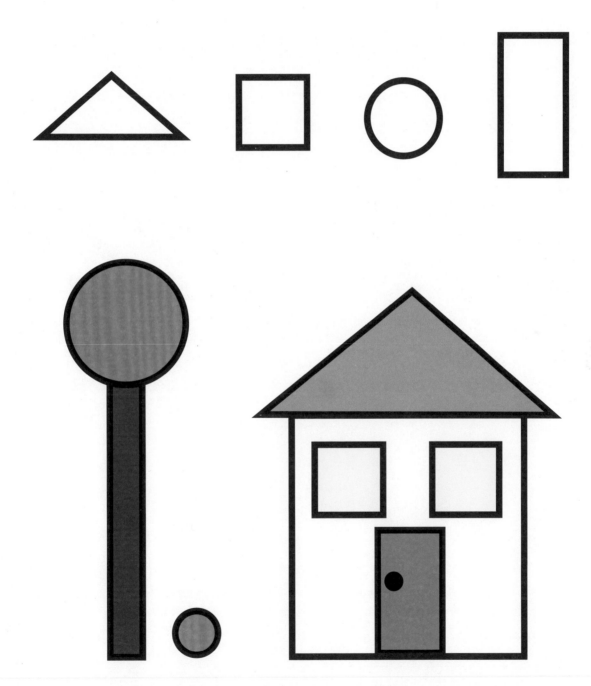

Point to the picture of the fewest pigs.

 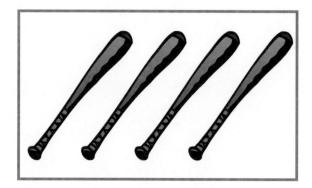

Point to the picture with the most bats.

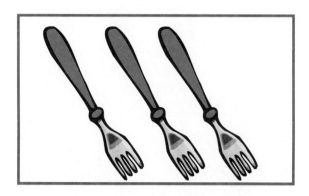 

Point to all the pictures with three things.

Lucky Dog

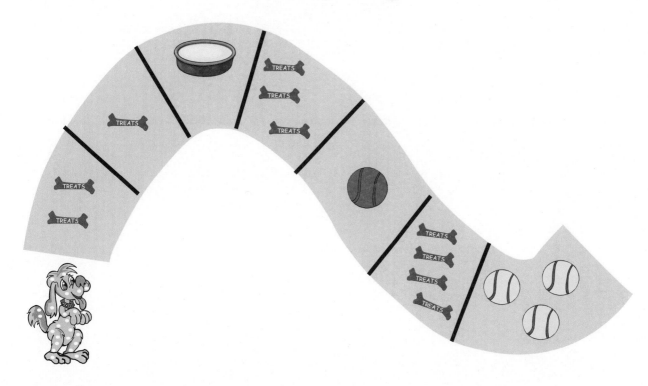

What will Spot find if he walks 2 spaces?

What will Spot find if he walks 5 spaces?

If Spot is thirsty, how many spaces must he walk?

How many spaces must Spot walk to find the space with the most bones?

What will Spot find if he walks 7 spaces?

Point to the picture that shows largest to smallest.
Point to the picture that shows smallest to largest.

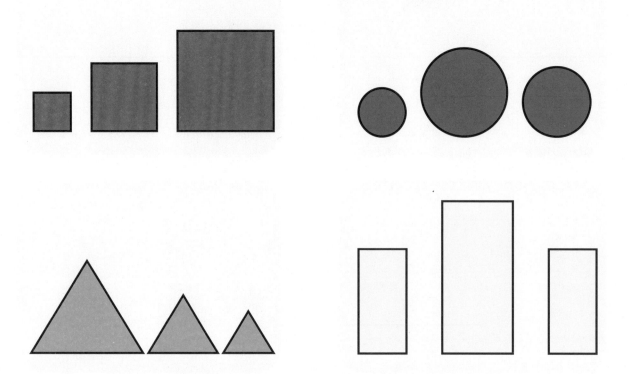

Draw three circles smallest to largest.

_____   _____   _____

1.   Which box has seven things?

2.   Which box has eight things?

3.   Which box has six things?

4.   Which box has the fewest things?

5.   Which box has the most things?

1. What is the blue shape below the green circle?

2. What is the red shape above the blue square?

3. What is the red shape to the right of the blue triangle?

4. What is the green shape to the left of the blue triangle?

Point to the picture that shows smallest to largest.
Point to the picture that shows tallest to shortest.

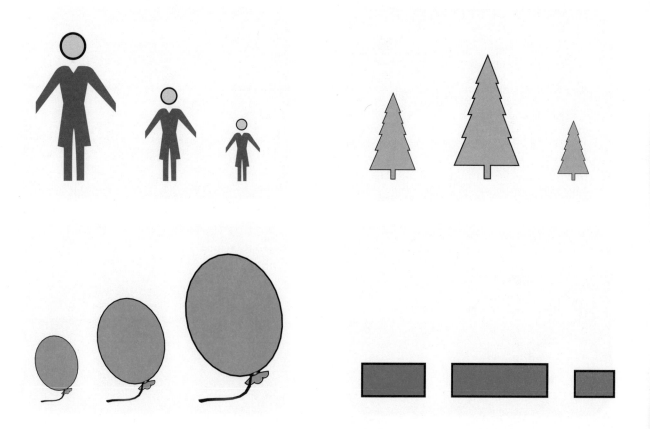

Complete the picture to show three triangles
shortest to tallest.

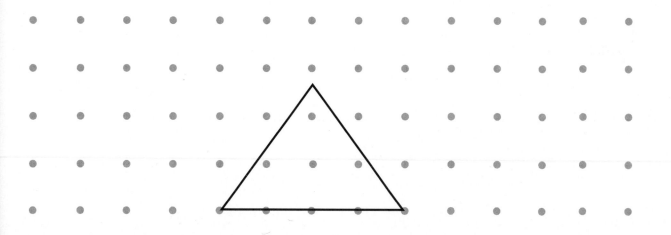

Write or say the number of objects in each box.

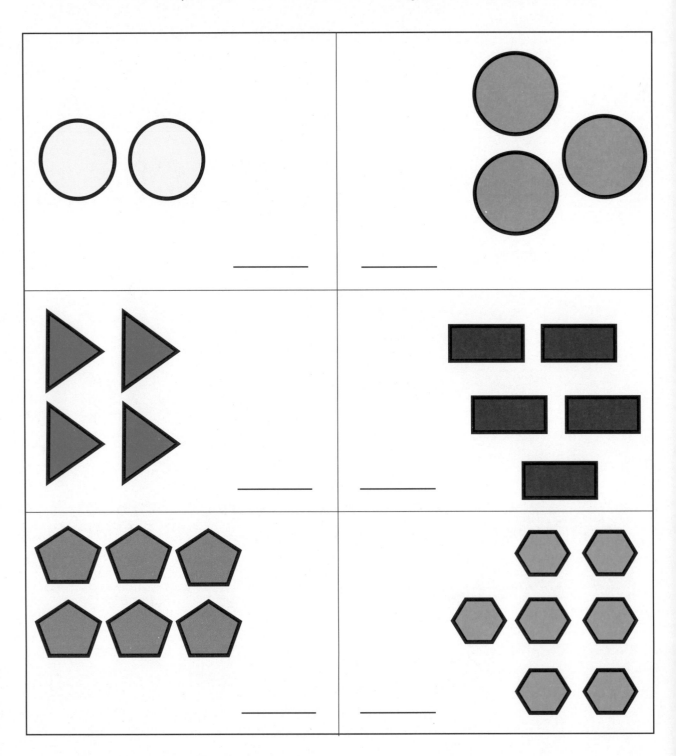

Mind Benders®*

A girl, a boy, and their dad each drank lemonade at lunch. Read the clues and fill in the chart using "Y" for yes and "N" for no to solve the puzzle.

1. The oldest drank the least.

2. The girl had the most glasses of lemonade.

Teaching Note: Teach your child to mark each yes and no answer learned from each clue. The problem is finished when all boxes are marked correctly.

*For more activities like this, please see our *Mind Benders®* series.

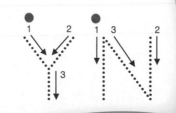

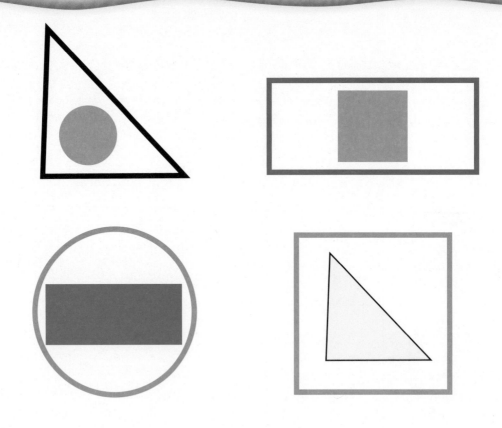

1. Point to the shape inside the circle.

2. Point to the shape outside the triangle.

3. Point to the shape inside the square.

4. Point to the shape outside the square.

5. Circle the shape inside the rectangle.

Use shape or color to split each row into two groups. Describe your group, then circle the groups.

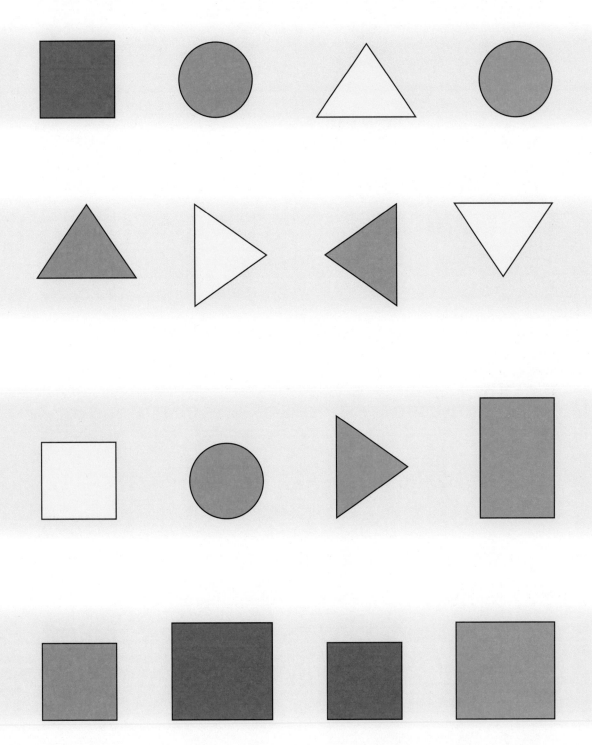

Teaching Note: There is no right answer. Your child could group by color, by shape, by objects that have corners, objects that do not have sharp corners, large and small, and so on. Any rational answer is acceptable provided your child can explain it.

1. How many brown horses are in the picture?

2. How many white horses are in the picture?

3. How many black horses are in the picture?

4. How many spotted horses are in the picture?

5. How many horses are in the picture?

6. If one horse is ridden way, how many horses are left?

7. If two horses are ridden away, how many horses are left?

Point to the slower object in each set of pictures.

Which figure does not belong?
Explain why it does not belong.

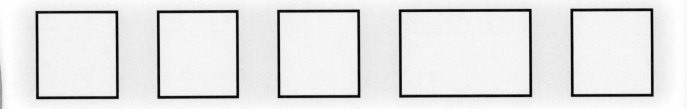

These are squares.

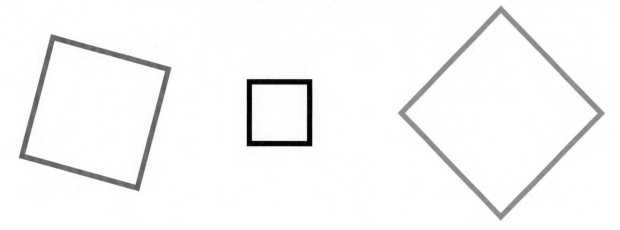

How many sides does a square have?

How many corners does a square have?

Draw 2 squares of the same size.

1. How many soccer balls are in the picture?

2. How many children are in the picture?

3. Draw a line segment connecting each soccer ball to a child.

4. How many children do not have soccer balls?

5. How many soccer balls do you need so that every child has a soccer ball?

A brother and a sister decided to divide these cookies.

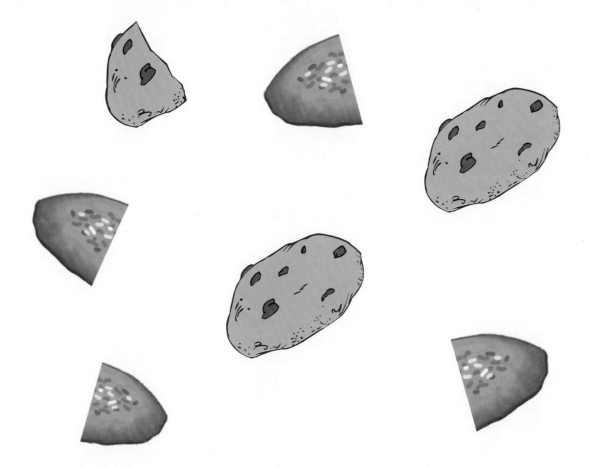

1. Jared's sister, Ali, took all the broken cookies. Draw a circle around each of Ali's cookies. How many broken cookies did she take?

   _____

2. Jared took all the cookies that were whole. Draw an X on each of Jared's cookies. How many whole cookies did he take?

   _____

There are four toys beside the boy.

There are two more toys in front of the boy.

1. Are there more toys beside the boy or in front of the boy?

2. If one toy was moved from beside the boy to in front of the boy, would more toys be in front of or beside the boy?

Divide each group into two groups. Explain how you made your groups.

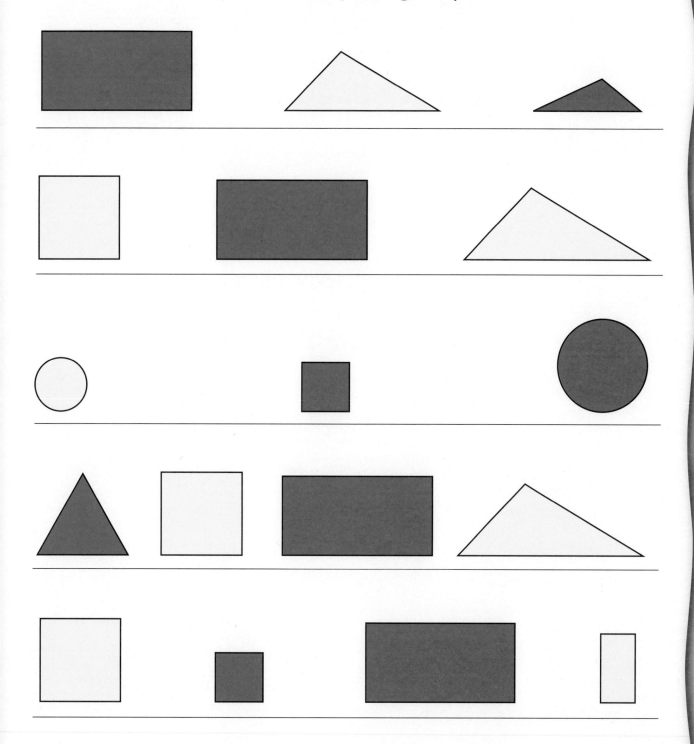

Teaching Note: There is no right answer. Any classification that can be rationally explained is acceptable. For example, classify the first group by color. This encourages communication, a fundamental tool in the study of mathematics.

How many cats? _____ Color the last two.

How many sailboats? _____ Color the one in the middle.

How many houses? _____ Color half of the houses.

1 2 3 4 5 6 7 8

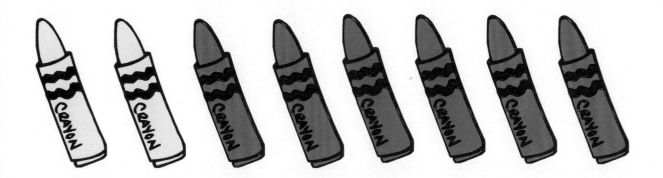

How many yellow crayons are there in the picture?

How many red crayons are there in the picture?

How many blue crayons are there in the picture?

How many crayons are there in the picture?

If you lost two crayons, how many crayons would you have?

Point to a circle on the clown's suit and say its color.

Point to a different circle on the clown's suit and say its color.

Point to a different circle on the clown's suit and say its color.

How many circles are on the clown's suit?

If all the blue circles are removed, how many circles would be left?

If all the blue circles and the red circles are removed, how many circles will be left?

1. How many straight sides in a square? Touch and count each straight side of each square.

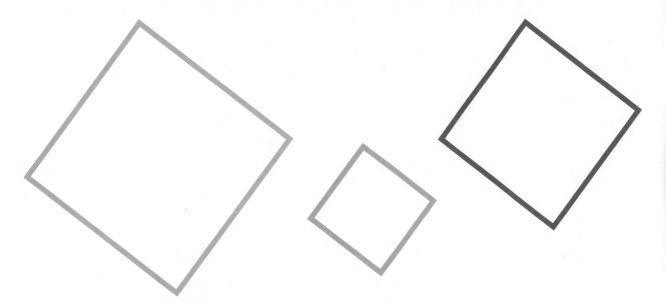

2. How many corners in a square? Touch and count the corners of each square.

3. Draw a square inside another square.

Find and count the shapes.

Triangles? _____ Circles? _____

Squares? _____ Rectangles? _____

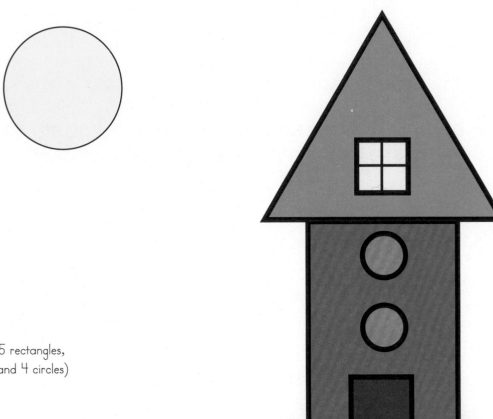

(5 squares, 5 rectangles,
3 triangles, and 4 circles)

3 4 5

Which figure does not belong? Explain why.

D D D ꓷ D

Ꟑ P P P P

Is the yellow flower near the mountains?

Is the tree near the mountains?

Is the house near the tree?

Are the mountains far from you?

Is the red flower far from you?

Is the red flower far from the mountains?

Is the tree near you?

Find something near you.

Find something far from you.

Circle the object that would be heaviest in each set of pictures. Put an X over the object that would be lightest in each set of pictures.

Circle the way you think the tack will land if it is dropped.

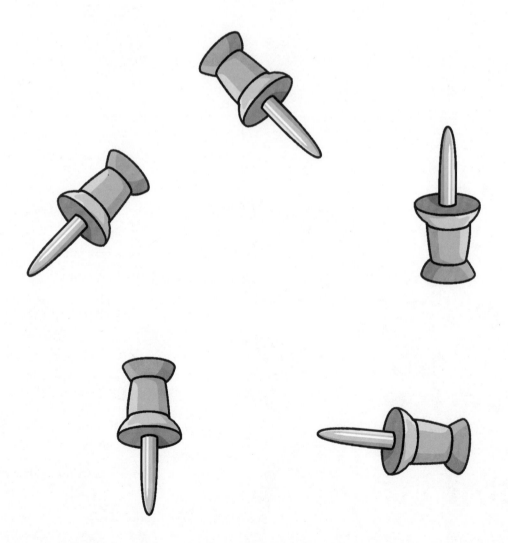

Write the total number of circles in each group.

1 2 3 4 5 6

Three friends ate these treats at the movies.

1. How many boxes of popcorn were eaten? __2__
   Shade the box on the chart to show that number.
   (Answer marked in blue on chart.)

2. Shade the other boxes on the chart to show the
   number of each kind of treat that was eaten.

3. Circle the treat that was bought the most.

4. Put an X on the treat that was bought the least.

Cross out animals to make the picture match the numeral below it.

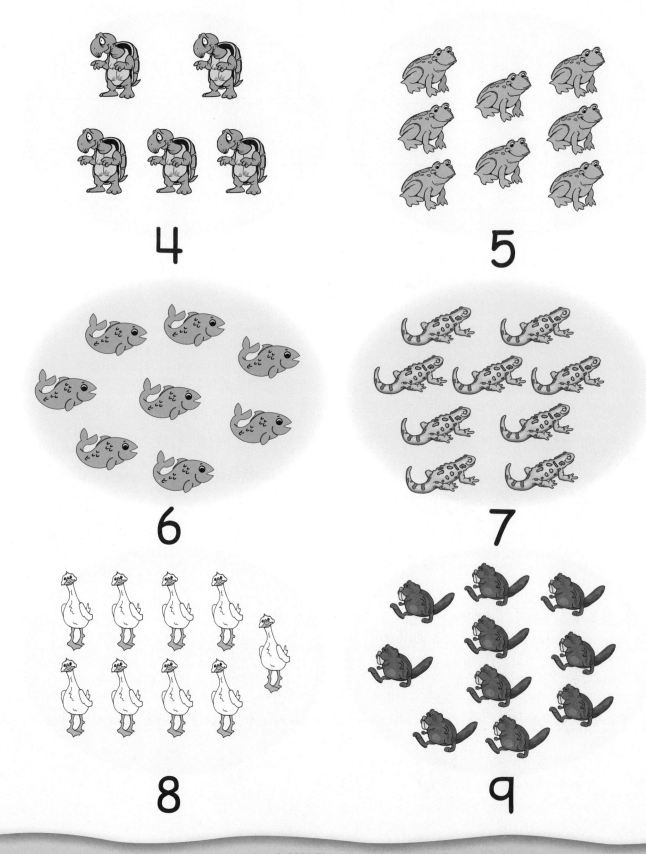

4

5

6

7

8

9

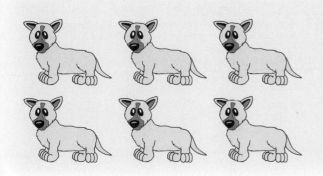

How many dogs are in the picture?
How many cats are in the picture?
How many animals are in the picture?

How many cows are in the picture?
How many horses are in the picture?
How many animals are in the picture?

Say the name of each number word listed below and have your child point to it on the number line and say its name.

Six

Nine

Five

Four

Two

Eight

One

Seven

Three

Zero

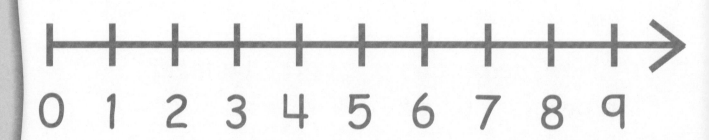

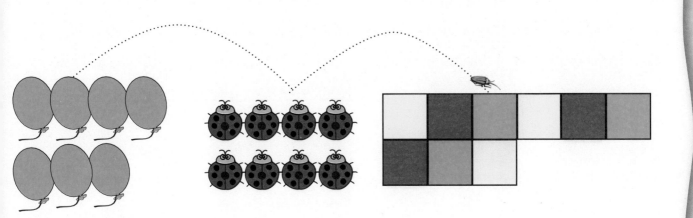

1. Point to the picture that has seven things in it.

2. Point to the picture that has eight things in it.

3. Point to the picture that has nine things in it.

4. Point to the picture that has the fewest things in it.

5. Point to the picture that has the most things in it.

6. Did the bug fly from the most to the fewest things or from the fewest to the most things?

Count ten (10) boats.
Touch and say the numbers.

1   2   3   4   5   6   7   8   9   10

Check the groups of 10.

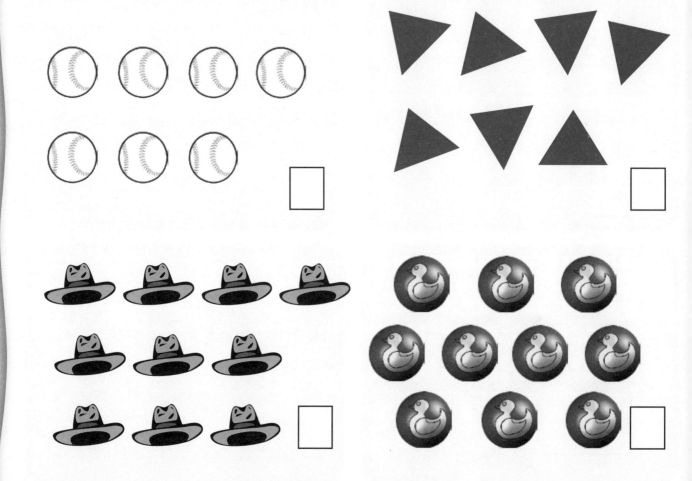

Connect each numeral to the same number of dots.

8

6

10

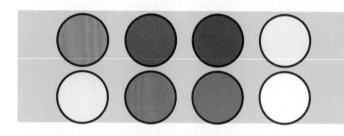

7

9

How many bugs are in the picture?

How many frogs are in the picture?

Draw segments between each frog and a
bug so each frog gets one bug.

Are there any frogs without bugs?

How many extra bugs are there?

Touch each figure and say its color and shape.

How many blue birds are in the picture?

How many green parrots are in the picture?

How many birds are in the picture?

How many green snakes are in the picture?

How many black snakes are in the picture?

How many snakes are in the picture?

Say each number word below and have your child point to the next larger value on the number line and say its name.

Six

Nine

Five

Four

Two

Eight

One

Seven

Three

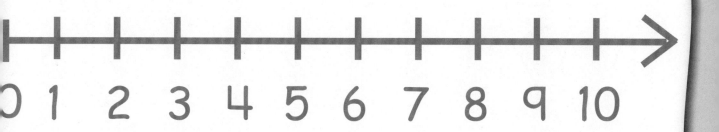

Draw a line segment to connect the groups with the correct numeral.

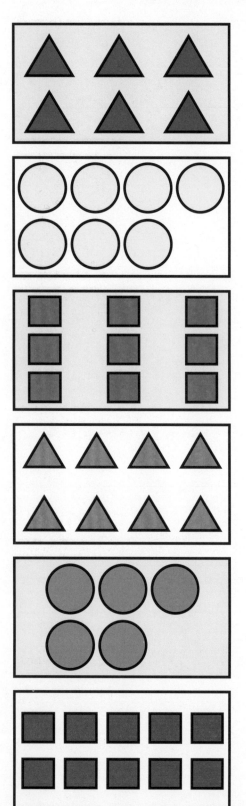

Point to the boy first in line for an apple and say the color of his pants.

Point to the boy third in line and say the color of his shirt.

Point to the the boy fourth in line and say the color of his cap.

Point to the boy second in line and say the color of his shirt.

Point to the boy second in line and say the color of his pants.

How many basketballs are orange?

Color more to make 9 orange basketballs

How many candies are green?

Color more to make 10 green candies.

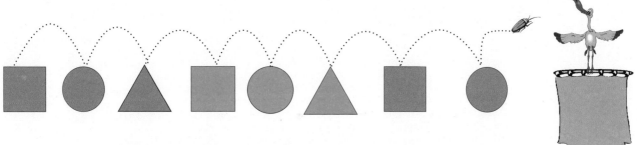

What shape would be next in the pattern?
What shape would be next after that?

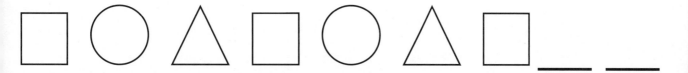

Finish the last two pictures to continue the pattern.

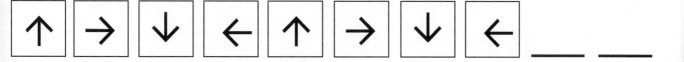

Finish the last two pictures to continue the pattern.

1. Which group is in smallest to largest order?
2. Which group is in largest to smallest order?

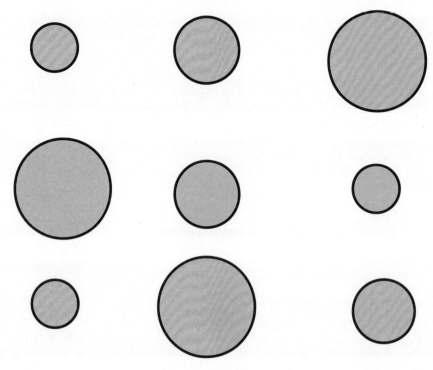

1. Which group is in smallest to largest order?
2. Which group is in largest to smallest order?

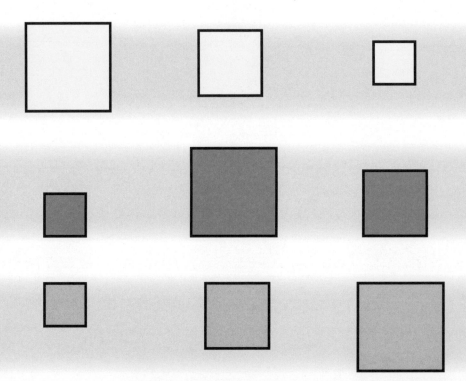

1. Are there more toys beside the girl or in front of the girl?

2. If you put the teddy bear in front of the girl, how many toys would be beside the girl?

3. If you moved one toy from beside the girl to in front of the girl, would more toys be in front of the girl or beside the girl?

4. When all of the toys are together, do you have an odd number of toys or an even number of toys? How can you tell?

Circle the objects in smallest to largest order.

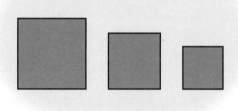

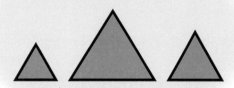

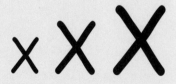

How many red triangles are in the picture?
How many blue triangles are in the picture?
How many triangles are in the picture?

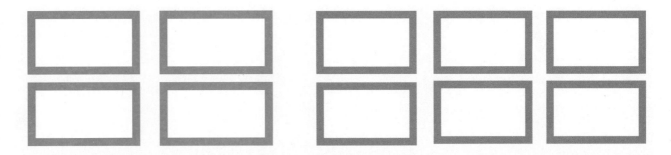

How many green rectangles are in the picture?
How many orange rectangles are in the picture?
How many rectangles are in the picture?

How many blue squares are in the picture?
How many green squares are in the picture?
How many rectangles are in the picture?

Teaching Note: All squares are rectangles. A square is a special type of rectangle.

These are rectangles.

Point to and count the sides of each rectangle.

Point to and count the corners of each rectangle.

Draw a small rectangle inside of another rectangle.

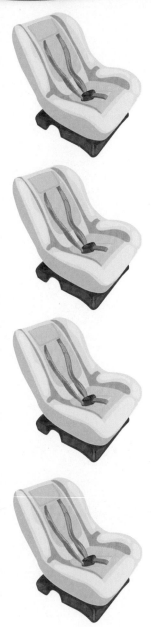

How many babies are in the picture?

How many car seats are in the picture?

Draw a line segment between each car seat and a baby, so each baby gets a car seat.

Circle the number of babies without car seats.

1   2   3   4   5   6

These are circles.

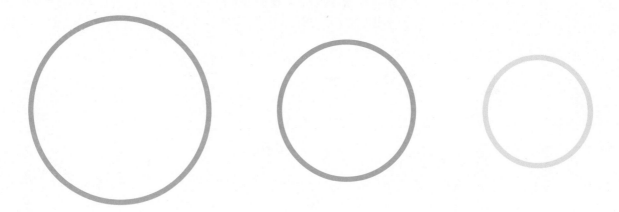

How many sides does a circle have?

How many corners does a circle have?

Draw 3 circles in smallest to biggest order.

_____   _____   _____

Cross out bugs to make the picture match the numeral below it.

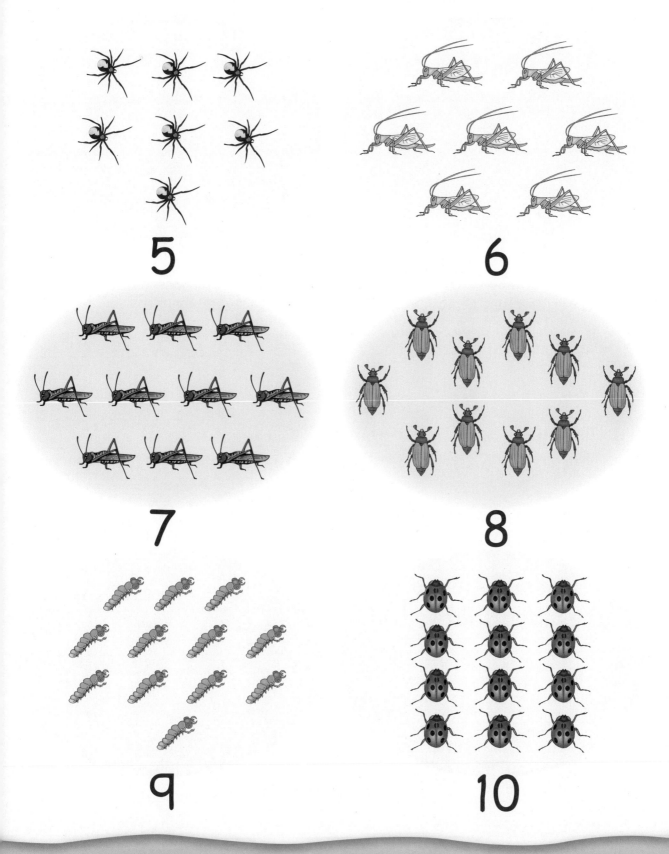

5

6

7

8

9

10

1. I'm thinking of a number that is
   after 1 and before 3. What's my number?_____

2. I'm thinking of a number that is after
   4 and before 6. What's my number? _____

3. I'm thinking of a number that is
   before 9 and after 7. What's my number? _____

4. How many elephants have
   a number that is before 7? _____

1 2 3 4 5 6 7 8

Point to the picture of 4 dogs.
Point to the picture of 6 dogs.
Circle the total number of dogs in both pictures.

6 7 8 9 10

Point to the picture of 3 ducks.
Point to the picture of 4 ducks.
Point to the picture of 2 ducks.
Circle the total number of ducks in all the pictures.

6 7 8 9 10

Draw a rectangle and a circle.

Draw a triangle inside a square.

Which girl will touch the water first?
What color is her bathing suit?

Which girl will touch the water third?
What color is her bathing suit?

Which girl will touch the water fourth?
What color is her bathing suit?

Which girl will touch the water second?
What color is her bathing suit?

Circle the number of girls in the picture.

4 5 6 7 8 9 10

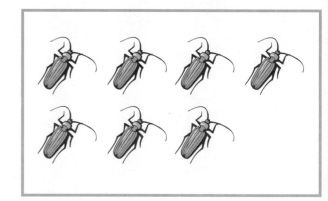

1. Point to the picture that has 5 things in it.

2. Point to the picture that has 6 things in it.

3. Point to the picture that has 7 things in it.

4. Point to the picture that has 8 things in it.

5. Point to the picture that has the fewest things in it.

6. Point to the picture that has the most things in it.

Smarty Pants Puzzles™

Answer the questions and point to things in the picture that helped you answer the questions.

1. What will the men eat for dinner?

2. Are the men waiting to catch their first fish?

3. How many fish have the men eaten?

4. How many men are in this group? Why do you think there are only two? (2 men, 2 plates, 2 fishing poles, 2 eaten fish.)

5. Does one man do all the fishing? (Yes, if he owns both poles; no, if the unused pole belongs to the other man.)

How many brown horses are in the picture?
How many white horses are in the picture?
How many black horses are in the picture?
How many gray horses are in the picture?
Circle the number of horses in the picture.

5 6 7 8 9 10

If one horse runs away, circle the number of horses left.

5 6 7 8 9 10

What is the color and shape to the right of the boy's hand?

What is the color and shape to the left of the boy's foot?

What is the color and shape to the left of the boy's hand?

What is the color and shape to the right of the boy's foot?

What is the color of the shape below the boy?
Name that shape.

How many red fish are in the picture?

How many black fish are in the picture?

Which color fish are the most?

Which color fish are the least?

How many fish are in the picture?

If the yellow fish are moved to their own fish bowl, how many fish would be in each bowl?

How many fish would be in both bowls?

Connect each dog to the right number of bones.

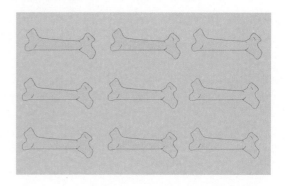

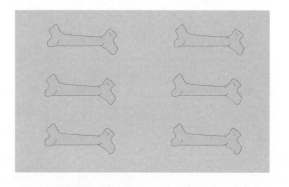

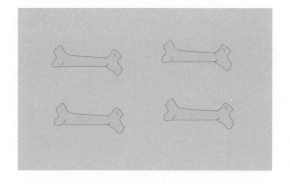

1. Spot has 4 bones.

2. Brownie has 2 more bones than Spot.

3. Blackie has 3 more bones than Brownie.

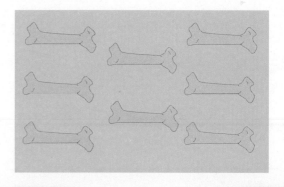

Point to and say the color of

- the largest circle

- the smallest triangle

- the largest square

- the smallest circle

- the largest rectangle

- the smallest square

- the largest triangle

- the smallest rectangle

Thinker Doodles™*

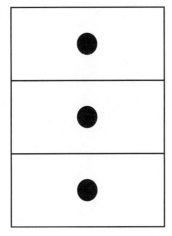 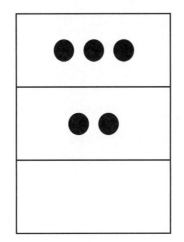 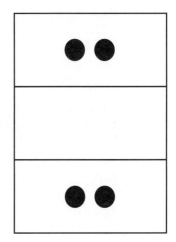

1. Look at each picture above, then find its unfinished picture below. Use a pencil to draw in all of the missing parts.

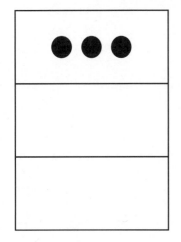 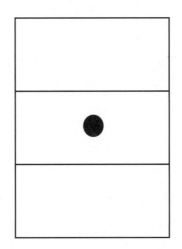 

2. Draw more dots so all of the pictures have 5 dots.

*For more activities like this, please see our *Thinker Doodles*™ series.

Point and count aloud, then write the number.

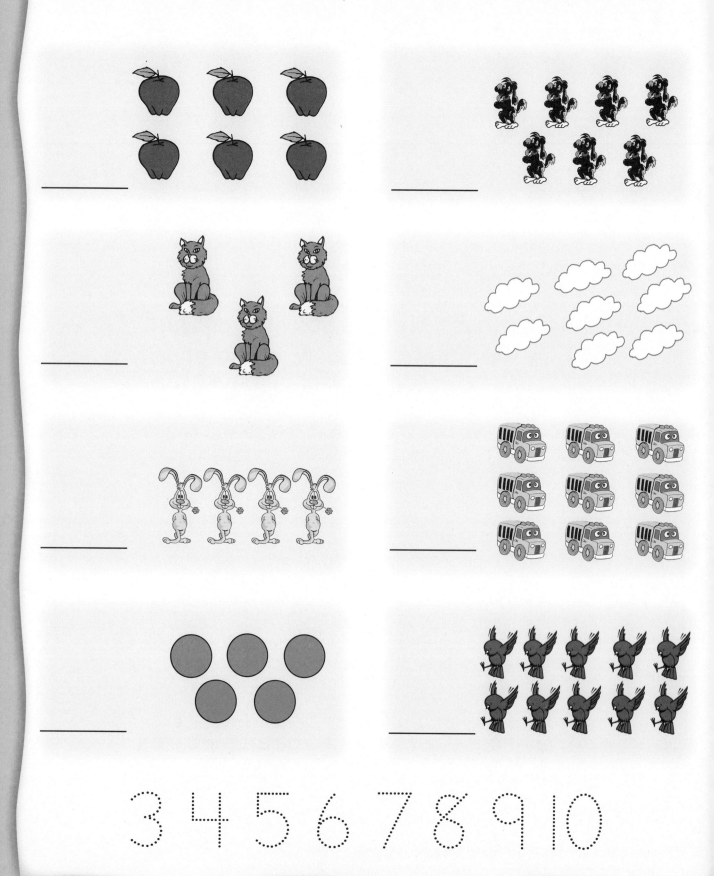

CAN YOU FIND ME?™*

If I cut four
there will still be more,
but only a few,
and a few would be two.

Of the three pictures that you see,
tell me now, can you find me?

*For more activities like this, see our *Can You Find Me?*™ series.

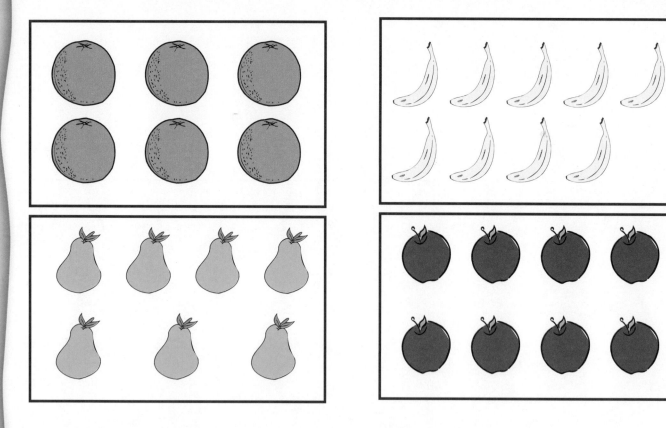

1. Point to the picture that has 6 things in it.

2. Point to the picture that has 7 things in it.

3. Point to the picture that has 8 things in it.

4. Point to the picture that has 9 things in it.

5. Point to the picture that has the fewest things in it.

6. Point to the picture that has the most things in it.

7. If you ate two bananas, how many would be left?

Teaching Note: If necessary, encourage your child to cross out two bananas, then count the remaining bananas.

Say each figure's numeral.

1. the purple ball
2. the blue kangaroo
3. the brown football
4. the yellow cat
5. the green leaf
6. the orange fish
7. the black bird
8. the red airplane
9. the green tree
10. the brown dog
11. the pink flower

Divide each group into two groups.
Explain how you made your groups.

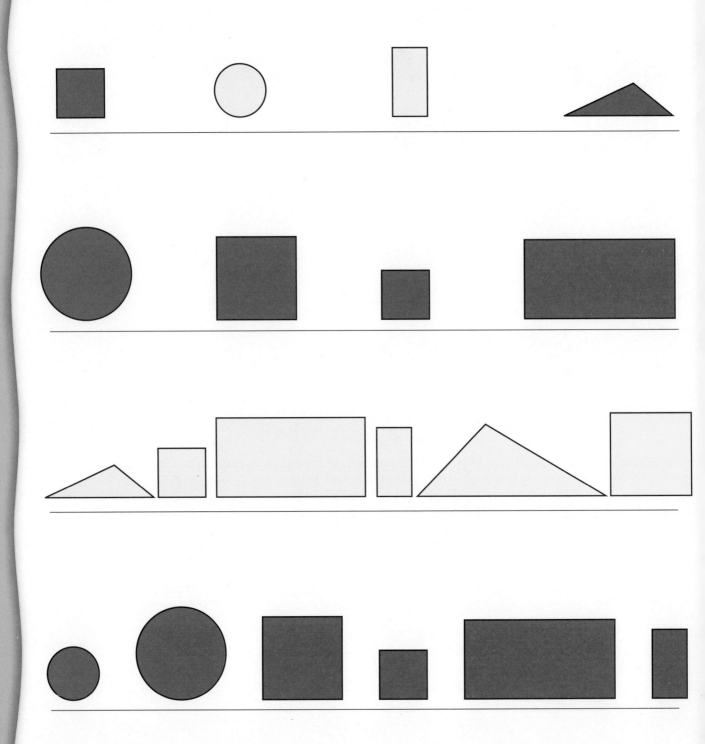

Teaching Note: There is no right answer. Any classification that can be rationally explained is acceptable. For example, classify the first group by color. This encourages communication, a fundamental tool in the study of mathematics.

1. Draw this group of circles in a different order. Explain your order.

(largest to smallest)

◯ ◯ ◯

_____ _____ _____

2. Draw these lines in two different orders. Explain each of your orders.

_____
_____
_____

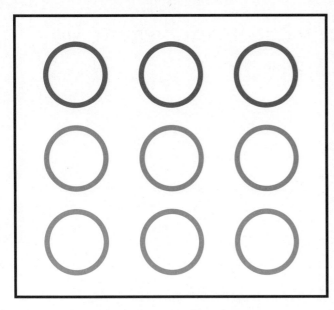 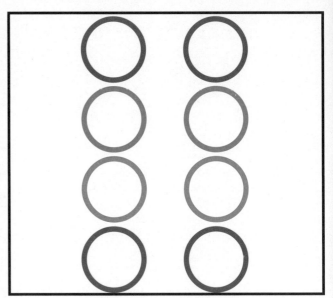

Point to the picture with the most red circles.
Circle the total number of red circles in both pictures.

5   6   7   8   9   10

Point to the picture with the most blue circles.
Circle the total number of blue circles in both pictures.

5   6   7   8   9   10

Point to the picture with the most green circles.
Circle the total number of green circles in both pictures.

5   6   7   8   9   10

Point to the picture with the least circles.

Circle the picture in each group that would be found in a colder place.

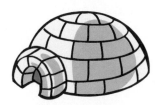 

Say each number word below and have the child point to and say any smaller value on the number line and say its name.

Six

Nine

Five

Four

Two

Eight

One

Seven

Three

Ten

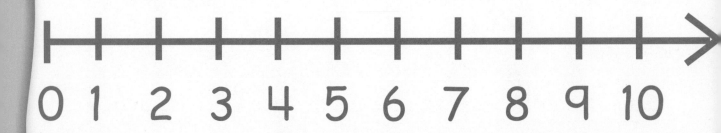

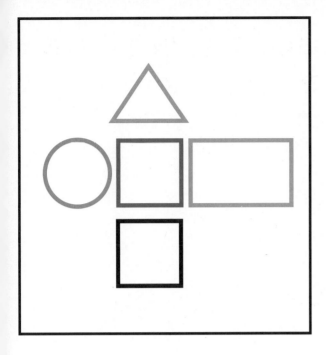

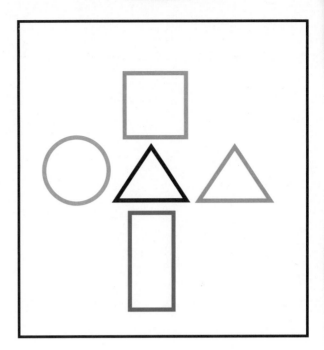

Say the color and shape left of the red square.

Say the color and shape below the black triangle.

Say the color and shape above the red square.

Say the color and shape right of the black triangle.

Say the color and shape above the black triangle.

Say the color and shape right of the red square.

Say the color and shape left of the black triangle.

Say the color and shape below the red square.

Draw a line segment from each numeral to the correct number of dots.

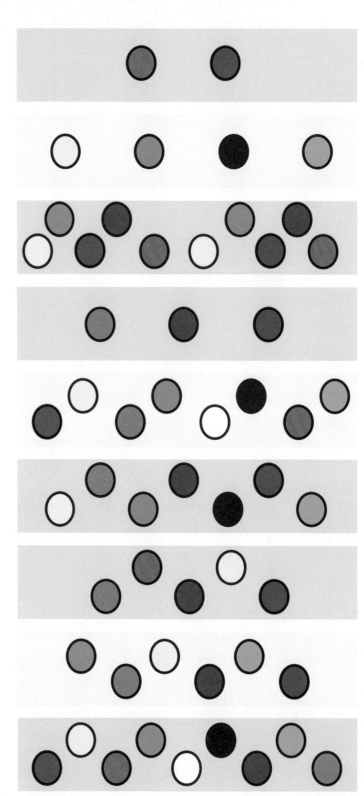

2

3

4

5

6

7

8

9

10

Smarty Pants Puzzles™

Answer each question and explain how you figured it out.

1. What are the names of the three friends above?

   Jan, Tom, and Mike <u>OR</u> Jan, Tom, and Michelle

2. What meal did the friends just finish eating?

   Breakfast   Lunch   Dinner

3. Only two children ate sandwiches. Which two children were they?

4. Only one child ate marshmallows. Which one was it?

5. What else do you think the children ate?

Draw line segments from each picture to the matching numeral.

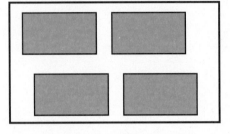

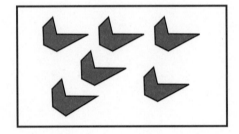

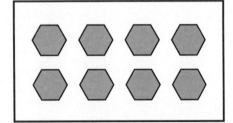

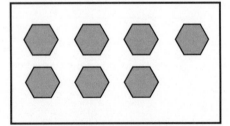

0

1

2

3

4

5

6

7

8

9

10

Left ⟷ Right

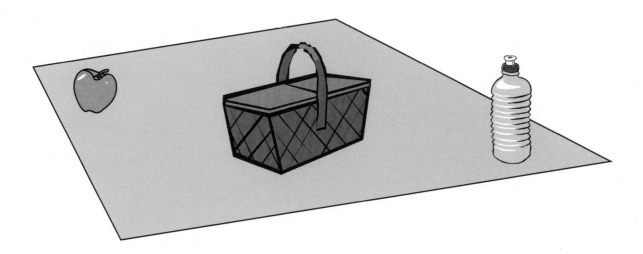

1. Circle the object that is to the right of the basket.

2. Put an X on the object that is to the left of the basket.

3. How many objects are on the cloth?

4. Circle the objects that are to the left of the water bottle.

5. Circle the objects that are to the right of the apple.

CAN YOU FIND ME?™*

I have fewer birds than Tim,
but two more than Jim.
Those are your clues,
who will you choose?

Of the four people that you see,
tell me now, can you find me?

*For more activities like this, see our *Can You Find Me?*™ series.

Half 'n Half Animals™*

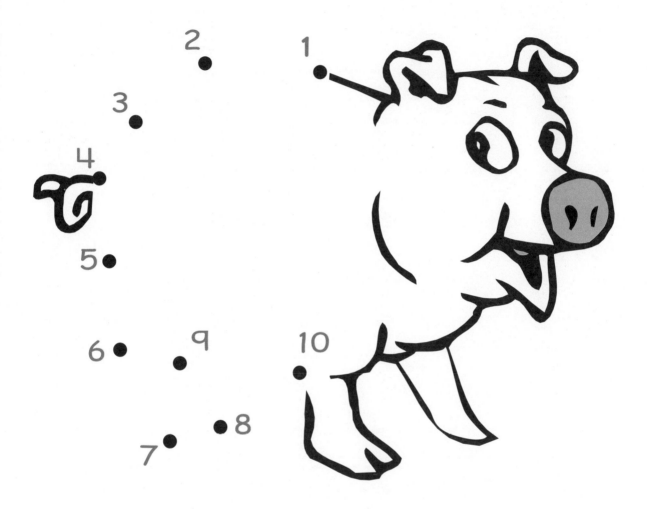

I live on a farm and like to play in the mud.

Connect the dots from 1-10, then color the picture. Can you add something else to the picture?

*For more activities like this, please see our *Half 'n Half Animals™* series.

Thinker Doodles™*

1. Look at each ladybug above, then find its unfinished picture below.
   Use a pencil to draw in all the missing parts.

2. Color the ladybugs with 3 dark circles using 3 colors.

3. Color the ladybugs with the most white circles using 4 colors.

*For more activities like this, please see our *Thinker Doodles™* series.

Draw a line segment to connect each picture with the matching numeral.

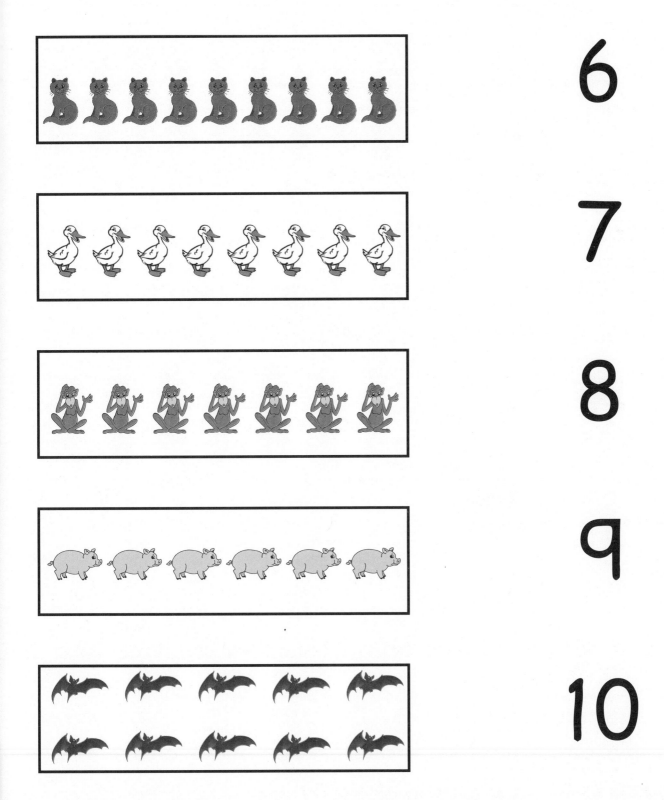

Make 10

How many lemons are yellow?

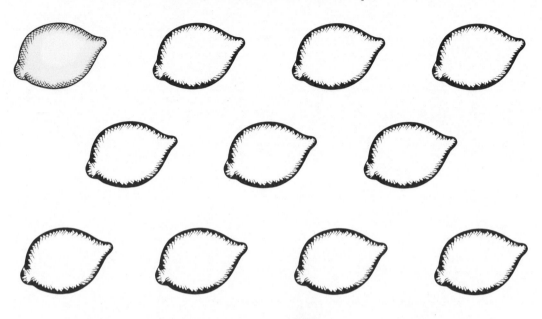

Color more to make 10 yellow lemons.

How many strawberries are red?

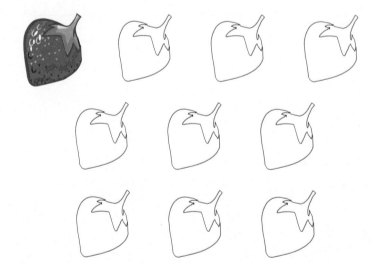

Color more to make 10 red strawberries.

Counting Rhyme

One, two, three, four, five,
Once I caught a fish alive.

Six, seven, eight, nine, ten,
Then I let it go again.

Why did you let it go?
Because it bit my finger so.

Which finger did it bite?
This little finger on the right.

Say the name of each number word below and have the child point to the next smallest value on the number line and say its name.

Six

Nine

Five

Four

Two

Eight

One

Seven

Three

Ten

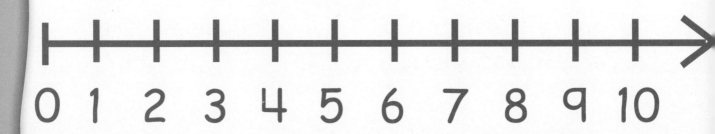

Half 'n Half Animals*

When I grow up, my wool will be used to make clothes.

Connect the dots 1-10, then color the picture. Can you add something else to the picture?

*For more activities like this, please see our *Half 'n Half Animals* series.

Count eleven (11) stars.

1 2 3 4 5 6 7 8 9 10 11

Cross out or draw circles to make the picture match the numeral below it.

11

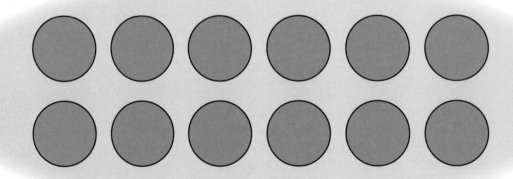

10

Circle each group of 10.
Check the groups of 11.

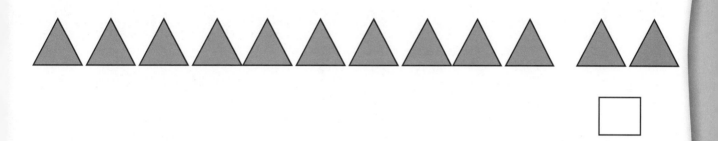

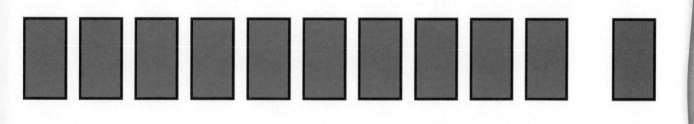

Cross out animals to make the picture match the numeral below it.

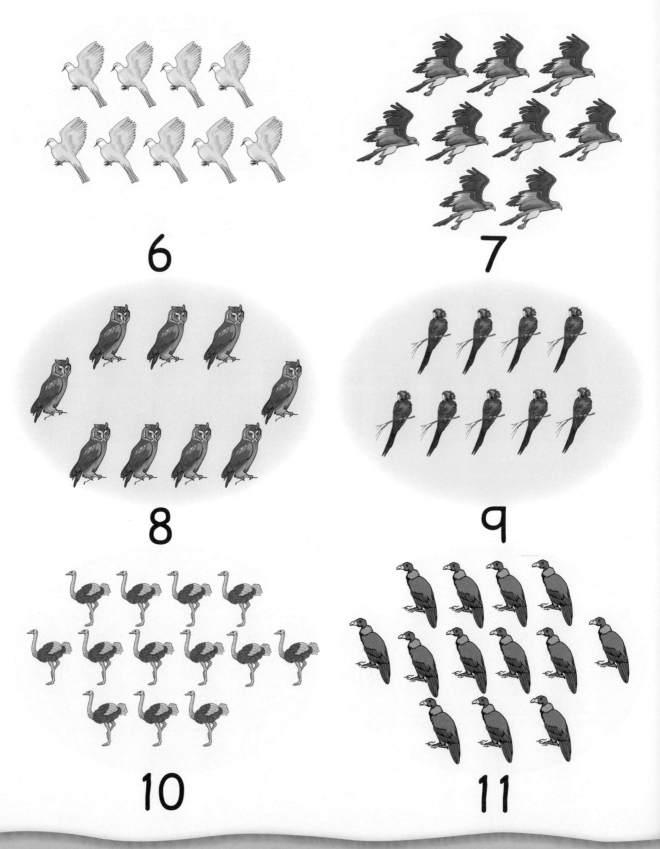

6

7

8

9

10

11

Connect the dots by counting from 1 to 11.

6 •
5 •   • 7
  4 •   • 8
    3 •   • 9
    2 •   • 10
      1 • • 11

Draw 11 balls and color eight of them.

1. Count the objects in each group below and in the groups on the next page. Write how many are in each group.

How many? _____

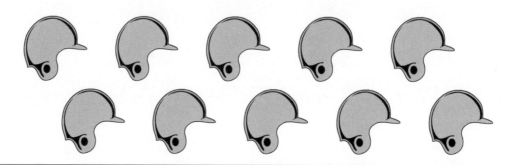

How many? _____

How many? _____

8   9   10   11

How many? _____

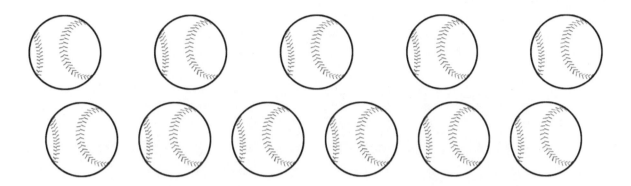

2. Circle the group that has the same number of objects as the group of bats.

3. Circle the group that has one more than the group of bats.

4. Circle the group that has one less than the group of bats.

1. Count the objects in the groups below and in the groups on the next page. Write how many are in each group.

How many? _____

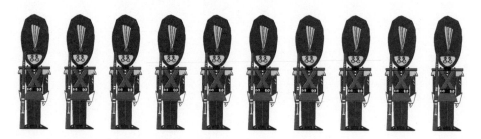

How many? _____

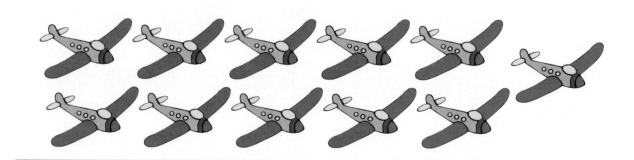

How many? _____

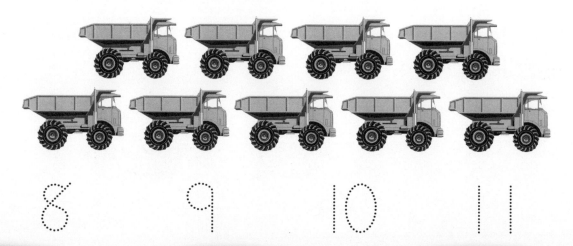

8   9   10   11

How many? _____

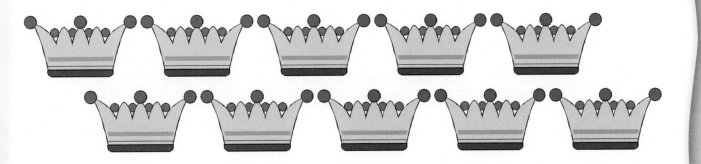

2. Circle the group that has the same number of objects as the toy soldier group.

3. Circle the group that has one more than the toy soldier group.

4. Circle the group that has one less than the toy soldier group.

Point to and say the shape of each object in each set. Tell how you would use color or shape to split each set into two groups.

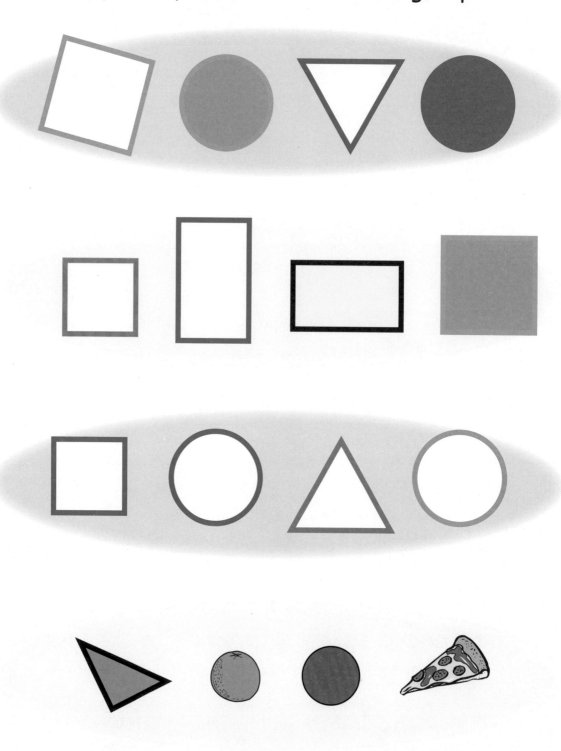

Teaching Note: There is no right answer. Any classification that can be rationally explained is acceptable. For example, classify the first group by color. This encourages communication, a fundamental tool in the study of mathematics.

1. How many children are in the picture?

2. How many ends are there on the teeter-totters in the picture?

3. Point to where each child needs to sit to make each teeter-totter work.

4. Can all the children play on the teeter-totters at the same time?

Put an X over the one that doesn't belong. Explain why the object does not belong.

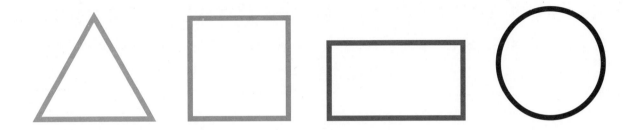

1. Say the name of the two shapes with the same number of sides.

2. Say the name of the two shapes with the same number of corners.

3. Which shape has three sides?

4. Which shape has three corners?

5. Draw a shape below with four sides and four corners.

Touch and say the name of each object in the pattern. Then say the name of the object behind the *yellow* curtain that will continue the pattern.

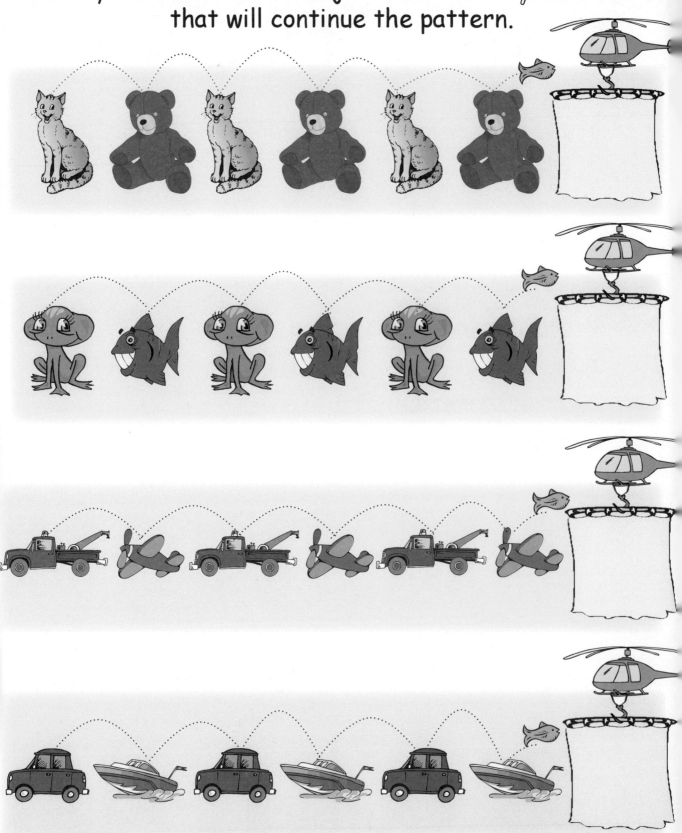

Count 12 apples.

1   2   3   4   5   6   7   8   9   10   11   12

Cross out or draw circles to make the picture match the numeral below it.

12

11

Circle each group of 10.
Check each group of 12.

When I say a number, point to a larger one on the number line.

Six

Nine

Five

Four

Two

Eight

One

Seven

Three

Zero

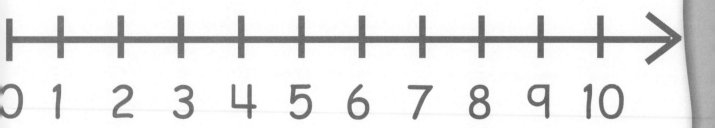

Touch and count 12 apples in each group.
Cross out any extra apples.

1. Terry is having a lemonade sale. Count,
    then write how many cups he wants to sell. _____

2. At the end of the day, Terry had
    sold 8 cups. How many cups were not sold? _____

Teaching Note: If necessary, encourage your child to cross out the sold cups to find the number of unsold cups.

Count 13 horses.

1　2　3　4　5　6　7　8　9　10　11　12　13

Cross out or draw dots to make the picture match the numeral below it.

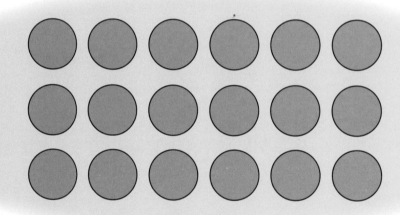

13

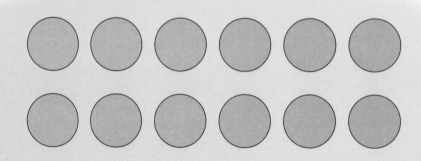

13

Circle each group of 10.
Check each group of 13.

Draw a line segment from each numeral to its picture.

12

11

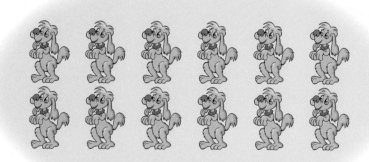

13

Circle the correct numeral in each group.

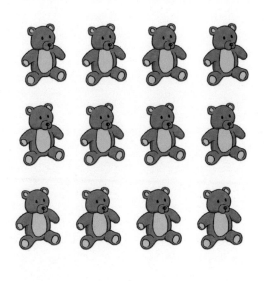

11   12   13

11   12   13

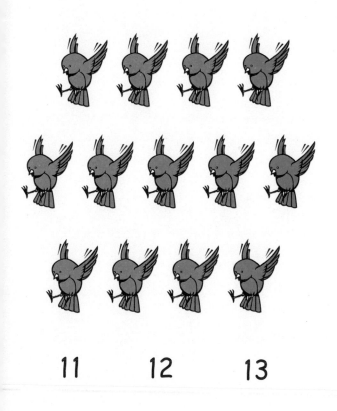

11   12   13

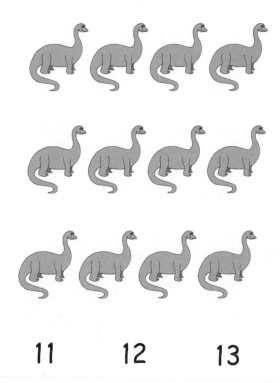

11   12   13

Point to the giraffe and answer each question.

Which giraffe is the tallest?

Which giraffe is the shortest?

Which giraffes are not the tallest?

Which giraffes are not the shortest?

Which giraffes are the middle sized ones?

Which giraffes are next to the tallest?

Which giraffe is next to the shortest?

Make up a question about the giraffes and ask someone to answer it.

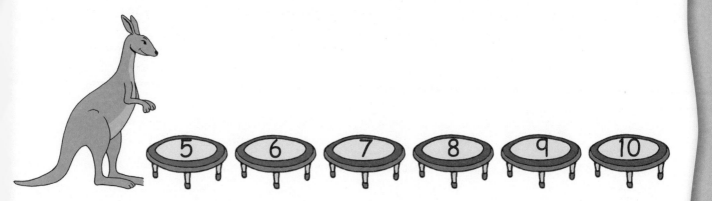

1. If Blue Kangaroo hops to 7 and then hops 1 more space, which number will he land on? _____

2. If Blue Kangaroo hops to 9 and then hops back 1 space, which number will he land on? _____

3. If Blue Kangaroo hops to 10 and then hops back 1 space, which number will he land on? _____

4. If Blue Kangaroo hops to 8 and then hops back 2 spaces, which number will he land on? _____

5. If Blue Kangaroo hops to 10 and then hops back 2 spaces, which number will he land on? _____

Complete each pattern with crayons.

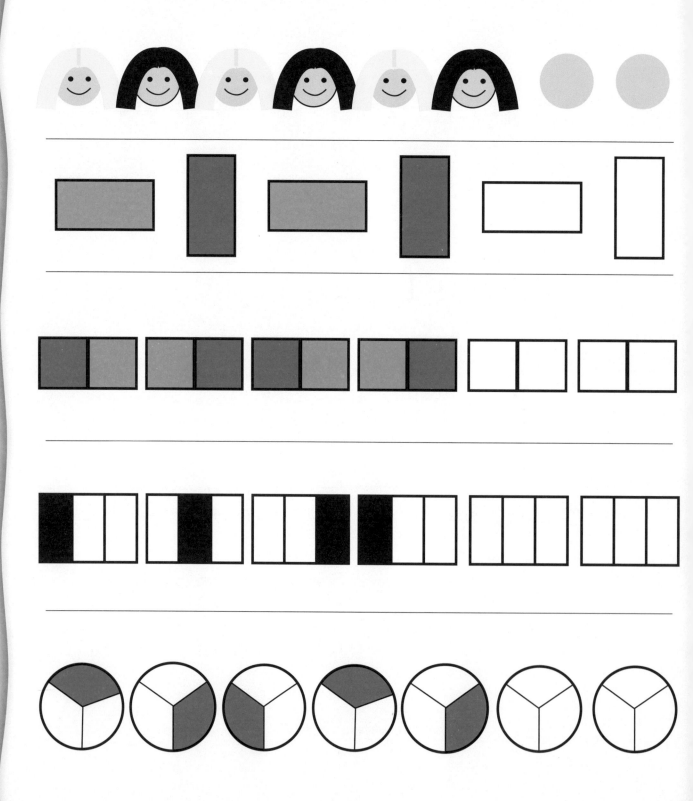

When I say a number, point to the one that is one more on the number line and say its name.

One, Three, Six, Ten, Four, Eight, Seven, Nine, Two, Zero, Five

Mind Benders®*

A girl, a boy, and a policeman all live in different houses. Read the clues and fill in the chart using "Y" for yes and "N" for no to solve the puzzle.

1. The policeman's house has fewer than 3 windows.

2. The girl's house has the most windows.

Teaching Note: Teach your child to mark each yes and no answer learned from each clue. The problem is finished when all boxes are marked correctly.

*For more activities like this, please see our *Mind Benders®* series.

Thinker Doodles™*

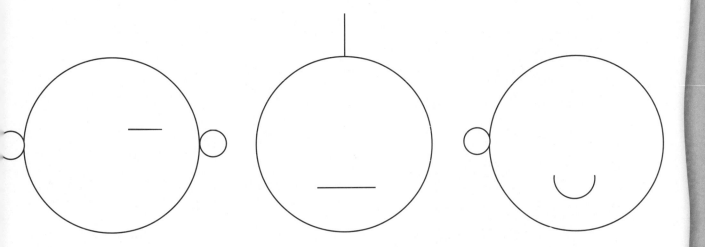

1. Look at each face above, then find its unfinished picture
   below. Use a pencil to draw in all the missing parts.

2. Color the faces with less than 3 hairs using 4 colors.

3. Color the faces with 3 hairs using 3 colors.

*For more activities like this, please see our *Thinker Doodles™* series.

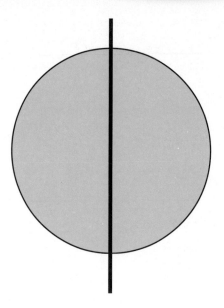

The line segment through the circle cuts
the circle into halves.
Draw a line segment that divides
each shape into 2 halves.

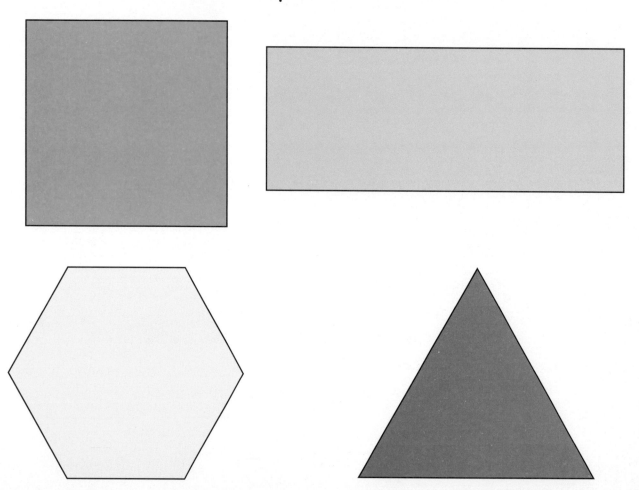

CAN YOU FIND ME?™*

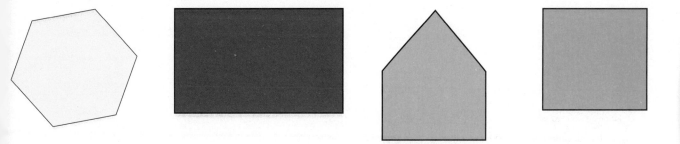

I am not red.

I am not blue.

But I have more sides

Than either of those two.

Of the four shapes that you see,

Tell me now, can you find me?

Draw a line segment to cut each piece of food in half (two equal parts).

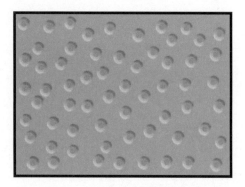

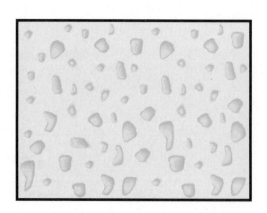

When I say a number, point to the one that is one more on the number line and say its name.

One, Three, Six, Four, Eight, Seven, Nine, Two, Zero, Five

Smarty Pants Puzzles™

Answer the questions and point to things in the picture that helped you answer the questions. These three friends all like different types of racing.

1. Which person rides an animal?

2. Which person does not ride on something when she is racing?

3. Which person is the fastest racer?

4. Which person is the slowest racer?

5. Which person is the second fastest racer?

Circle ten cars, then touch and count the fourteen (14) cars.

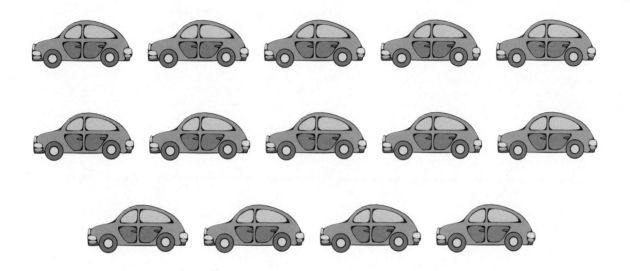

Circle ten balloons, then touch and count the fifteen (15) balloons.

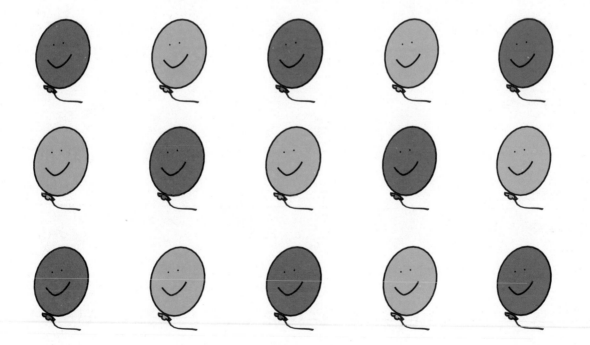

Touch and count each group of pictures.

13

14

15

When I say a number, point to it on the number line and say its name.

One, Three, Six, Ten, Four, Eight, Seven, Nine, Two, Zero, Five

Mind Benders®*

Three fish all ate flies for dinner. Find out how many flies each fish ate. Read the clues and fill in the chart using "Y" for yes and "N" for no to solve the puzzle.

1. The longest fish had more than 3 flies.

2. The shortest fish had more than two flies.

Teaching Note: Teach your child to mark each yes and no answer learned from each clue. The problem is finished when all boxes are marked correctly.

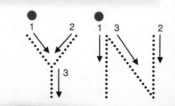

*For more activities like this, please see our *Mind Benders®* series.

Circle the correct numeral in each group.

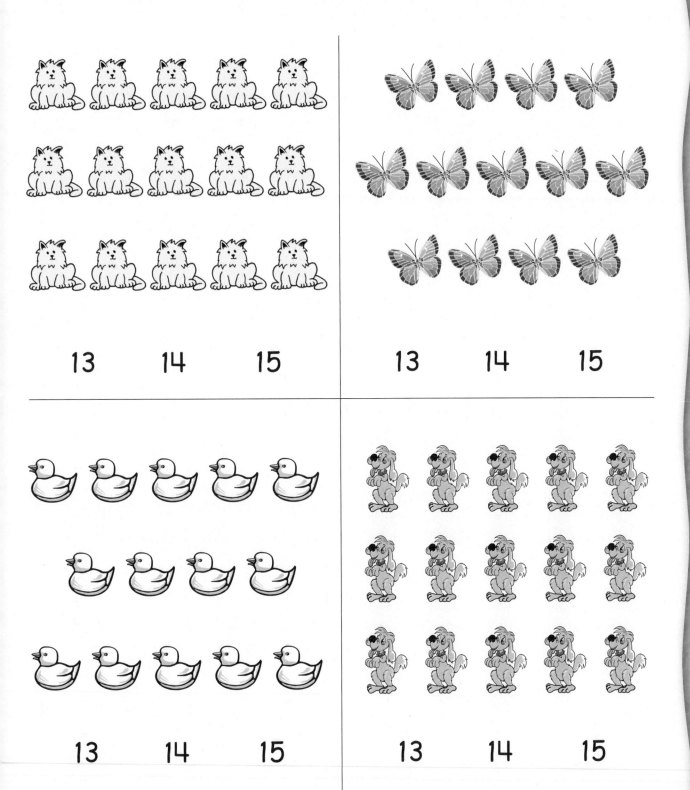

13   14   15

13   14   15

13   14   15

13   14   15

When I say a number, point to the one that is one less on the number line and say its name.

One, Three, Six, Ten, Four, Eight, Seven, Nine, Two, Five

Touch and say the name of each item in the pattern. Then say the name of the object behind the green curtain.

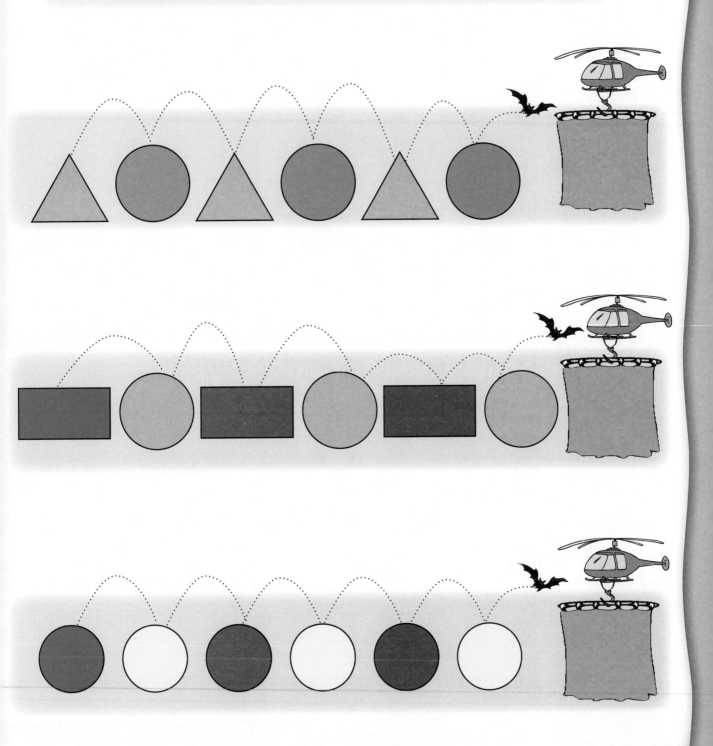

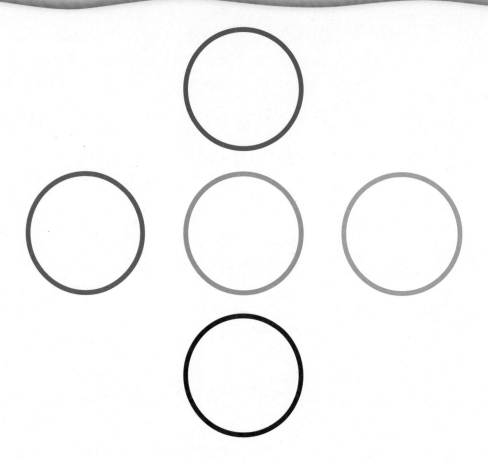

1. How many circles are in the picture?

2. What color circle is in the middle of the picture?

3. What color circle is above the green circle?

4. What two circles are beside the green circle?

5. What color circle is below the green circle?

6. How many circles are next to the green circle?

Mind Benders®*

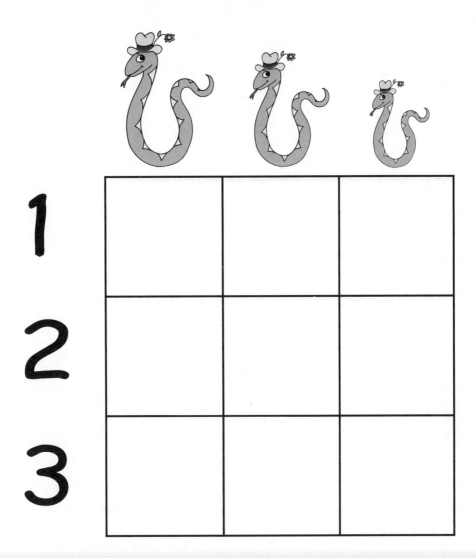

Three snakes all have different ages (1, 2, 3). Read the clues and fill in the chart using "Y" for yes and "N" for no to solve the puzzle.

1. The longest snake is not the youngest.

2. The shortest snake will be 3 next year.

Teaching Note: Teach your child to mark each yes and no answer learned from each clue. The problem is finished when all boxes are marked correctly.

*For more activities like this, please see our *Mind Benders®* series.

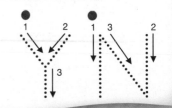

When I say a number, point to the one that is one mo
on the number line and say its name.

One, Three, Six, Five, Four, Eight, Seven, Nine, Two, Zero